CHARLES D. FIELD

ERNEST HEMINGWAY

COLLECTION

To Willie Rakow
best always from his
friend.
Ernest Hemingway
Havana 9/8/54.

ERNEST M. HEMINGWAY, 1954

THE

ERNEST HEMINGWAY

COLLECTION

of

CHARLES D. FIELD

Catalogue prepared by Bonnie D. Cherrin

STANFORD UNIVERSITY LIBRARIES

Stanford, California

1985

ISBN 0-911221-05-0

CONTENTS

INTRODUCTION

THE Charles D. Field Collection of Ernest Hemingway has been some twenty-five years in the making. Beginning with Charles Field's interest in the life and writings of one of America's pre-eminent authors, the Field Collection has grown to include a generous harvest of first editions, translations, articles, and galley proofs covering virtually all of Hemingway's printed output. With its numerous inscribed copies of notable editions, unpublished letters and documents, and manuscript fragments, the collection also captures the flavor of Hemingway the man—outspoken, direct, vigorous—and his relationships with friends and colleagues. In terms of its scope and content, the Field Collection of Ernest Hemingway is a significant achievement in book collecting and a creation of permanent value to scholars.

Charles Field had a partner in this enterprise, the distinguished San Francisco bookseller, Warren R. Howell. The Field Collection is an especially fine example of the way in which the close collaboration between collector and bookseller can result in an important library. It had been Charles Field's hope that Warren Howell would write the introduction to this catalogue. Unfortunately, Warren's death intervened. However, several years ago Warren did contribute a piece on Charles Field to *Imprint*, the publication of the Associates of the Stanford

University Libraries. A version of that article was recently found in Warren's files. It is a personal memoir in which Warren's voice can be unmistakably heard:

"I have known Charles Field for many years. On many occasions we would show up at the same social functions in San Francisco in the late '30s and '40s. At these casual meetings, there was no opportunity for us to get down to the discussion of books. So it was a most pleasant surprise when Charlie walked into the book shop one day in 1957 and began to tell me of his great interest in Ernest Hemingway. Charles had read a great many of Hemingway's books and having enjoyed them so much he felt that this was the time to begin collecting these books in their first editions. He wanted advice and help in putting together a collection. At that time he probably was not aware that collecting all the items he wanted would become so involved and *take so much time.*

"Since that day of our first talk about Hemingway in 1957, we have worked hard to find good collectors' copies of the first editions of Hemingway. I have searched for so much Hemingway everywhere I go that I got a reputation for grabbing all of the good books and letters by Hemingway to place in Charles' collection. It has been fortunate that others have realized how seriously I pursued Hemingway items for this encouraged people to offer many choice items to us. The first expensive item we secured for Charlie was a six-page letter of Hemingway's to Louis and Mary Bromfield, written on typical yellow paper in 1926 and full of advice to Bromfield about his writing and how to get it published. Carlos Baker, the biographer of Hemingway, heard about that letter and asked for a copy of it. Later, Baker sold me all of the correspondence he had with Hemingway. These items were placed with Charlie."

The publication of this catalogue marks the gift of the Hemingway Collection to the Stanford University Libraries. In transferring this fine collection to Stanford, Charles Field wants to bring it more into the view of scholars by placing it in the context of a major research library. This is the latest of many gifts to Stanford which Charles and his wife Frances have made in support of teaching and research at the University, and the Library is particularly grateful for their ongoing thoughtfulness and generosity.

Michael T. Ryan
Curator of Special Collections
Stanford University Libraries

EDITORIAL NOTE

SINCE the Field Collection is an author collection, this catalogue has been generally organized to conform to author bibliographies. Part I is an inventory of Hemingway's writing, containing five subsections. Section A includes American, English and English language editions of Hemingway's books, arranged chronologically according to the date of their first publication. Section B is a chronological listing of first appearances and reprints of poems, short stories and articles in books, pamphlets, newspapers and periodicals, as well as Hemingway's contributions (introductions, prefaces, etc.) to works by other authors. Section C is comprised of translations of Hemingway's works, organized alphabetically by language, then chronologically by date of publication. Both Section D— Adaptations (mostly screenplays) — and Section E — Ephemera — are ordered chronologically.

Part II, listing primarily biographical and bibliographical material on, about or relating to Hemingway, includes two subsections. Section A is arranged alphabetically by author or editor and is devoted to books and pamphlets. Section B is organized chronologically and includes newspaper and periodical material followed by ephemera.

Part III, with three subsections, is an inventory of Hemingway letters and manuscripts in the Field Collection. Section A contains both outgoing and incoming correspondence in one series, ordered alphabetically by recipient in the former case and alphabetically by writer in the latter. Section B, organized chronologically, includes manuscript material and one document. Section C lists correspondence relating to Hemingway alphabetically by writer.

Part IV is devoted to art work portraying Hemingway.

All attempts to supply missing names, dates, and places are indicated by brackets, as are other editorial additions.

Items in the collection which are reported in Audre Hanneman's *Ernest Hemingway: A Comprehensive Bibliography* (Princeton: Princeton University Press, 1967) and the *Supplement to Ernest Hemingway: A Comprehensive Bibliography* (Princeton: Princeton University Press, 1975) are indicated by the bibliography's number (*e.g.,* AIA for *Bibliography,* Sup AIA for *Supplement*) at the end of the entry.

Likewise, letters in the collection which have been published in Carlos Baker's *Ernest Hemingway: Selected Letters, 1917–1961* (New York: Charles Scribner's Sons, 1981) are indicated by the appropriate page numbers (*e.g.,* CB194–196) at the conclusion of the citation.

Thanks and appreciation are extended to Franklin E. Huffman, Professor of Linguistics and Asian Studies, Cornell University; Edward Jajko, Middle East Bibliographer, Hoover Institution, Stanford University; Mark Tam, Deputy Curator, East Asian Collection, Hoover Institution, Stanford University; and Patricia Bialecki, Department of Special Collections, Stanford University Libraries, for their assistance in translation of foreign language editions of Hemingway's works.

All citations from unpublished Hemingway material are made with the kind permission of the author's literary executors.

PART I

Writings by Hemingway

A.
BOOKS AND PAMPHLETS:
American, English and English Language Editions

B.
CONTRIBUTIONS AND FIRST APPEARANCES

C.
TRANSLATIONS

D.
ADAPTATIONS

E.
EPHEMERA

PART I:A

BOOKS AND PAMPHLETS

American, English and English Language Editions

---

1. *Three Stories and Ten Poems*
   [Paris]: Contact Publishing Company, 1923
   First limited edition
   Paper covers
   A1A

2. *Three Stories and Ten Poems*
   Bloomfield Hills, Michigan: Bruccoli Clark Books, 1977
   Facsimile edition
   Blue cloth with dust jacket
   Facsimile of first limited edition (No. 1)

3. *in our time*
   Paris: Three Mountains Press, 1924
   First limited edition
   Number 62 of 170 copies
   INSCRIBED: "Bill Bird made the cover of the book and had the
       woodcut made from a portrait by Henry (Mike) Strater—Mike
       did not like the woodcut which he said was lousy—He painted
       the portrait in Rapallo in February of 1923 I believe—most of
       this book was written before then—Ernest Hemingway"
   Tan boards
   A2A

4. *in our time*
   Bloomfield Hills, Michigan: Bruccoli Clark Books, 1977
   Facsimile edition
   Red cloth with dust jacket
   Facsimile of first limited edition (No. 3)

5. *In Our Time*

New York: Charles Scribner's Sons, 1930
Second American edition, revised
Introduction by Edmund Wilson
Black cloth with dust jacket
A3B

6. *In Our Time*

Paris: Crosby Continental Editions, 1932
Reprint edition
Paper covers
A3C

7. Another copy

INSCRIBED: "To Whitney Darrow with many thanks and good wishes Ernest Hemingway"

8. *The Torrents of Spring*

A Romantic Novel in Honor of the Passing of a Great Race
New York: Charles Scribner's Sons, 1926
First edition
SIGNED: "Ernest Hemingway New York 1928"
Dark green cloth with dust jacket
A4A

9. Another copy

INSCRIBED: "To O. J. Kadlec with all good wishes Ernest Hemingway"; on the first page of text: "Paris"

10. *The Torrents of Spring*

A Romantic Novel in Honor of the Passing of a Great Race
Paris: Crosby Continental Editions, 1932
Reprint edition
Introductory "Open Letter to Ernest Hemingway" by Caresse Crosby, Paris, December 1931
Paper covers
A4B

11. *The Torrents of Spring*

A Romantic Novel in Honor of the Passing of a Great Race
Taipei: Tun-huang shu chü, 1969

Introduction by David Garnett
Green cloth with dust jacket
Piracy of A37B?

12. *The Torrents of Spring*

A Romantic Novel in Honor of the Passing of a Great Race
New York: Charles Scribner's Sons, 1972
Paperback edition
Sup AID

13. *Today Is Friday*

Englewood, New Jersey: The As Stable Publications, 1926
First edition
Number 135 of 300 copies
Drawing by Jean Cocteau
INSCRIBED: "To Dr. Guffey from his friend Ernest Hemingway"
Paper wrappers
A5A

14. *The Sun Also Rises*

New York: Charles Scribner's Sons, 1926
First edition
Black cloth with dust jacket
A6A

15. *Fiesta*

[*The Sun Also Rises*]
London: Jonathan Cape, 1927
First English edition, second impression
INSCRIBED: "To [Detzel] and Garfield also regretting the expenditure Ernest"
Blue cloth
A33A

16. *The Sun Also Rises*

New York: The Modern Library, 1930
Reprint edition
Introduction by Henry Seidel Canby
Maroon cloth with dust jacket
A6B

17. *The Sun Also Rises*

New York: Grosset & Dunlap, 1930
Reprint edition
Black cloth with dust jacket
A6c

18. *The Sun Also Rises*

New York: Bantam Books, 1949
Paperback edition
A6G

19. *Fiesta*

[*The Sun Also Rises*]
London: Pan Books, 1951
English paperback edition
A33C
Hanneman dates this edition 1952

20. *Men Without Women*

New York: Charles Scribner's Sons, 1927
First edition
Black cloth with dust jacket
A7A

21. *Men Without Women*

London: Jonathan Cape, 1928
First English edition
INSCRIBED: "To [Detzel] and Garfield regretting that they
   bought it—Ernest"
Blue cloth
A34A

22. Another copy

INSCRIBED: "To C. S. Collinson Esq. very truly, Ernest Hemingway"
Blue cloth with dust jacket

23. *Men Without Women*

New York: Charles Scribner's Sons, 1932
First edition, third issue

INSCRIBED: "To Irving Reis with very best wish [sic] from his
    friend and admirer Ernest Hemingway"

Black cloth

A7A

24. *Men Without Women*

Cleveland and New York: The World Publishing Company, 1946
Illustrated by John Groth
Red cloth with dust jacket

A7E

25. Another copy

INSCRIBED: "For Emeline and Vic with best Christmas greetings
    from Charles Sweeny and Ernest Hemingway

26. *A Farewell to Arms*

New York: Charles Scribner's Sons, 1929
First edition
Black cloth with dust jacket

A8A

27. *A Farewell to Arms*

New York: Charles Scribner's Sons, 1929
Limited edition
Number 341 of 510 copies, signed by the author
Green boards, gold and red slipcase

A8B

28. Another copy

Number 431 of 510 copies, signed by the author
Green boards with dust jacket, gold and red slipcase

29. *A Farewell to Arms*

London: Jonathan Cape, 1929
First English edition
INSCRIBED: "To C. S. Collinson, Esq. with the best wishes of the
    author Ernest Hemingway"
Purple cloth with dust jacket

A35A

30. *A Farewell to Arms*

Leipzig: Bernhard Tauchnitz, 1930
Reprint edition

INSCRIBED: "For Mr. Booth—Claire Ballard"
Blue cloth and leather
A8c; variant binding; lacking "32 pages of advertisements" indicated in Hanneman

31. *A Farewell to Arms*

Stockholm and London: Zephyr Books, The Continental Book Company AB, 1947
Reprint edition
INSCRIBED: "To Peter Russell wishing him all good fortune Ernest Hemingway. Cortina, 1949"
Paper covers with dust jacket

32. *A Farewell to Arms*

New York: Charles Scribner's Sons, 1948
Illustrated by Daniel Rasmusson
Grey cloth, grey slipcase
A8J

33. *A Farewell to Arms*

New York: Bantam Books, 1949
Paperback edition
A8K

34. *Introduction to Kiki of Montparnasse*

New York: Edward W. Titus, 1929
Introduction appeared in *Kiki's Memoirs* (No. 125)
Paper covers
A9

35. *Death in the Afternoon*

New York: Charles Scribner's Sons, 1932
INSCRIBED: "To Jane [Mason Gingrich] with love from Pappa"
Unbound first gathering with preliminaries

35a. *Death in the Afternoon*

New York: Charles Scribner's Sons, 1932
First edition
Color frontispiece of "The Bullfighter" by Juan Gris
Black cloth with dust jacket
A10A

36. Another copy
SIGNED: "Ernest Hemingway Cooke, Montana September 1932"

37. Another copy
INSCRIBED: "To Uncle Gus with much affection Ernest"

38. *Death in the Afternoon*
London: Jonathan Cape, 1932
First English edition
Color frontispiece of "The Bullfighter" by Juan Gris
Orange cloth with dust jacket
A36A

39. *God Rest You Merry Gentlemen*
New York: House of Books, Ltd., 1933
First limited edition
Number 82 of 300 copies
Red cloth
A11A

40. Another copy
Number 269 of 300 copies
INSCRIBED: "To Gus Best always Ernest Hemingway"
Red cloth with dust jacket

41. *Winner Take Nothing*
New York and London: Charles Scribner's Sons, 1933
First edition
Black cloth with dust jacket
A12A

42. *Green Hills of Africa*
[New York: Charles Scribner's Sons, 1935]
Galley proofs of chapters VI–XI, with printer's notes and indication that "original mss is 132 to 180"

42a. *Green Hills of Africa*
New York and London: Charles Scribner's Sons, 1935
First edition
Decorations by Edward Shenton
Green cloth with dust jacket
A13A

43. *Green Hills of Africa*
Garden City, New York: Permabooks, Doubleday & Company, 1954
Paperback edition
Decorations by Edward Shenton
A13D

44. *To Have and Have Not*
New York: Charles Scribner's Sons, 1937
First edition
Black cloth with dust jacket
A14A

45. *To Have and Have Not*
New York: Editions for the Armed Services, [1945?]
Armed Services edition
Paper covers
A14E

46. *To Have and Have Not*
Stockholm and London: Zephyr Books, The Continental Book Company AB, 1947
Reprint edition
INSCRIBED: "To Alden with love Ernest Hemingway"
Paper covers with dust jacket

47. *The Spanish Earth*
Cleveland: J. B. Savage Company, 1938
First edition
Introduction by Jasper Wood
Illustrations by Frederick K. Russell
INSCRIBED: "For my pal, Aunt Marie from her nephew Jap"
Unnumbered "Author's Copy"
Tan cloth with dust jacket
A15A

48. Another copy
Number 66 of 1000 copies

49. *The First 48*
[New York: Charles Scribner's Sons, 1938]
Galley proofs

50. *The Fifth Column and the First Forty-nine Stories*

New York: Charles Scribner's Sons, 1938
First edition
INSCRIBED: "To Garfield with best wishes always Ernest Hemingway"
Red cloth with dust jacket
A16A

51. *The Fifth Column and the First Forty-nine Stories*

New York: Charles Scribner's Sons, 1939
First edition, second issue
INSCRIBED: "To Charles Sweeny, Jr. from his friend Ernest Hemingway"
Red cloth
A16A

52. *The Fifth Column and the First Forty-nine Stories*

London: Jonathan Cape, 1939
First English edition
Tan cloth with dust jacket
A41A

53. *The Fifth Column*

A Play in Three Acts
[New York: Charles Scribner's Sons, 1940]
Galley proofs

54. *The Fifth Column*

A Play in Three Acts
New York: Charles Scribner's Sons, 1940
First separate edition
Grey cloth with dust jacket
A17A

55. *The Fifth Column*

London: Jonathan Cape, 1968
First English hard-cover edition
Black cloth with dust jacket
Sup A21F

56. *For Whom the Bell Tolls*
[New York: Charles Scribner's Sons, 1940]
Galley proofs

57. *For Whom the Bell Tolls*
Galley proofs bound with original printed front matter for Scribner's First Edition 'A'; original portrait photograph of Hemingway by Arnold inlaid in front pastedown
INSCRIBED: "Sun Valley, Idaho October 21, 1940 This book is for Taylor Williams, remembering all the good shots we've had together. Ernest Hemingway It is the only true First Edition copy of this book as it was bound from the original front matter and the corrected first page proofs. EH"
Green morocco

58. *For Whom the Bell Tolls*
New York: Charles Scribner's Sons, 1940
First edition
Tan cloth with dust jacket
A18A

59. Another copy
INSCRIBED: "For Garfield who was on our side in Spain best always Ernest Hemingway"

60. Another copy
INSCRIBED: "For Marcella Burns [Haliner] with very best regards from her old friend and admirer Ernest Hemingway"
Tan cloth

61. *For Whom the Bell Tolls*
New York: Charles Scribner's Sons, 1940
First edition, second issue
Tan cloth
A18A

62. Another copy
INSCRIBED: "For Captain and Mrs. W. [R]. H. Noble with sincere best wishes from their friend Ernest Hemingway"
Tan cloth with dust jacket

63. *For Whom the Bell Tolls*

London and Toronto: Jonathan Cape, 1941
First English edition
Blue cloth with dust jacket
A42A

64. *For Whom the Bell Tolls*

London: The Reprint Society, 1942
Reprint edition
Yellow cloth

65. *For Whom the Bell Tolls*

Stockholm: Zephyr Books, The Continental Book Company AB,
     1943
Reprint edition
Paper covers with dust jacket

66. *Men at War*

The Best War Stories of All Time
New York: Bramhall House, 1979
Reprint edition
Edited with an introduction by Ernest Hemingway
Planned by William Kozlenko
Black cloth with dust jacket

67. *Hemingway*

New York: The Viking Press, 1944
First edition
Malcolm Cowley, ed.
Red cloth with dust jacket
A22A

68. *Selected Short Stories*

New York: Editions for the Armed Services, [1945?]
Armed Services edition
Paper covers
A20A

69. *The Essential Hemingway*

Taipei: Tun-huang shu chü, 1967
Maroon cloth with dust jacket
Piracy of A43A?

70. *Across the River and Into the Trees*
>London: Jonathan Cape, 1950
>First edition, advance copy
>Paper covers with dust jacket
>A44A

71. *Across the River and Into the Trees*
>London: Jonathan Cape, 1950
>First edition
>Green cloth with dust jacket
>A44A

72. *Across the River and Into the Trees*
>[New York: Charles Scribner's Sons, 1950]
>Galley proofs dated September 7, 1950

73. *Across the River and Into the Trees*
>New York: Charles Scribner's Sons, 1950
>First American edition, advance copy
>INSCRIBED: "Advanced copy from which I reviewed *Across the
>   River* for Herald Tribune Books. Malcolm Cowley"
>Unbound with dust jacket

74. *Across the River and Into the Trees*
>New York: Charles Scribner's Sons, 1950
>First American edition
>Black cloth with dust jacket
>A23A

75. Another copy

76. *Across the River and Into the Trees*
>New York: Dell Publishing Company, 1953
>Paperback edition
>A23C

77. *The Old Man and the Sea*
>[New York: Charles Scribner's Sons, 1952]
>Galley proofs

78. *The Old Man and the Sea*
   New York: Charles Scribner's Sons, 1952
   First edition
   Blue cloth with dust jacket
   A24A

79. Another copy
   Signed by the author
   Black cloth
   Variant binding

80. *The Old Man and the Sea*
   London: Jonathan Cape, 1952
   First English edition
   Blue cloth with dust jacket
   A45A

81. Another copy
   INSCRIBED: "For Estelle with love Ernest"

82. *The Old Man and the Sea*
   New York: Charles Scribner's Sons, 1960
   College edition
   Blue cloth with dust jacket
   A24B

83. *The Old Man and the Sea*
   Franklin Center, Pennsylvania: The Franklin Library, 1975
   Limited edition
   Illustrated by Daniel Schwartz
   Blue leather

84. *The Hemingway Reader*
   New York: Charles Scribner's Sons, 1953
   First edition
   Charles Poore, ed.
   Red cloth with dust jacket
   A25A

85. *The Collected Poems of Ernest Hemingway*
   n.p., n.d.
   Pirated edition

The Library of Living Poetry, Number 1
Paper covers
A26B

86. Another copy

87. *The Collected Poems of Ernest Hemingway*
San Francisco, 1960
Pirated edition
Paper covers
A26C

88. Another copy

89. *Two Christmas Tales*
Berkeley, California: The Hart Press, 1959
Privately printed, limited edition
Illustrated by Victor Anderson
Paper covers
A27A

90. *The Wild Years*
New York: Dell Publishing Company, 1962
First edition
Gene Z. Hanrahan, ed.
Paper covers
A30A

91. Another copy

92. *A Moveable Feast*
New York: Charles Scribner's Sons, 1964
First edition
Brown and grey cloth with dust jacket
A31A

93. *A Moveable Feast*
[London: Jonathan Cape, 1964]
Galley proofs

94. *A Moveable Feast*
New York: Charles Scribner's Sons, 1971

Second paperback edition
Sup A13C

95. *By-Line, Ernest Hemingway*
Selected Articles and Dispatches of Four Decades
New York: Charles Scribner's Sons, 1967
First edition
William White, ed.
Red cloth with dust jacket
Sup A14A

96. Another copy

97. *Excerpts from* By-Line: Ernest Hemingway
Selected Articles and Dispatches of Four Decades
New York: Charles Scribner's Sons, 1967
William White, ed.
Eight-page promotional booklet containing nineteen short excerpts from *By-Line*; back cover photograph of Hemingway by Robert Capa
Paper covers
Sup A14A

98. *By-Line, Ernest Hemingway*
Selected Articles and Dispatches of Four Decades
London: William Collins Sons, 1968
First English edition
William White, ed.
Commentaries by Philip Young
INSCRIBED: "For John Holtzman: This completes your run of the firsts of *By-Line*: the Scribner, the Literary Guild, & now Collins. One hundred years from now a cataloguer will list this & say: 'signed by the editor.' Bill White, with regards. Detroit, 10 April 1968"
Orange cloth with dust jacket
Sup A26A

99. *The Undefeated*
Moscow: Higher School Publishing House, 1968
Paper covers

100. *The Fifth Column and Four Stories of the Spanish Civil War*
New York: Charles Scribner's Sons, 1969
First edition
Red cloth with dust jacket
Sup A15A

101. *Ernest Hemingway, Cub Reporter*
Kansas City Star *Stories*
Pittsburgh: University of Pittsburgh Press, 1970
First edition
Matthew J. Bruccoli, ed.
Blue and grey cloth with dust jacket
Sup A16A

102. *Islands in the Stream*
New York: Charles Scribner's Sons, 1970
First edition
Green cloth with dust jacket
Sup A17A

103. Another copy

104. *Islands in the Stream*
London: Book Club Associates, 1970
English Book Club edition
Blue cloth with dust jacket

105. *Islands in the Stream*
Toronto, New York and London: Bantam Books, 1972
Paperback edition
Sup A17A

106. *Ernest Hemingway's Apprenticeship*
Oak Park, 1916–1917
Washington, D.C.: NCR/Microcard Editions, 1971
Collector's edition
Matthew J. Bruccoli, ed.
Olive and blue cloth
Sup A18A

107. *The Nick Adams Stories*

New York: Charles Scribner's Sons, 1972
First edition
Preface by Philip Young
Blue cloth with dust jacket
Sup A19A

108. *The Nick Adams Stories*

New York: Charles Scribner's Sons, 1972
Book Club edition
Preface by Philip Young
Blue cloth with dust jacket
Sup A19A

109. *A Divine Gesture*

New York: Aloe Editions, 1974
Privately printed, limited edition
Number 36 of 250 copies
Paper covers

110. *The Snows of Kilimanjaro*

Cambridge: Syndics of the Cambridge University Press, 1975
Paper covers

111. *88 Poems*

New York and London: Harcourt Brace Jovanovich; Bruccoli
    Clark, 1979
First edition
Nicholas Gerogiannis, ed.
Brown cloth with dust jacket

112. *The Faithful Bull*

London: Hamish Hamilton, 1980
Limited edition
Number 3 of 100 copies, signed by the illustrator
Pictures by Michael Foreman
Woodcut 3/100 of "The Faithful Bull" by Michael Foreman in-
    cluded
Yellow boards, brown slipcase

PART I:B

CONTRIBUTIONS AND FIRST APPEARANCES

---

113. "Class Prophecy"
Article in *Senior Tabula*, June 1917, pp. 57–62
Paper covers
c31

114. Another copy

115. "Wanderings"
Poems in *Poetry, A Magazine of Verse* 21 (1923): 193–195
c121

116. "Pamplona Letter"
Article in *Transatlantic Review* 2 (1924): 300–302
c160

116a. [Part] III. [Appreciation of Conrad]
Article, *ibid.*, Joseph Conrad Supplement, pp. 341–342
c160

117. "The Undefeated"
Short story in *This Quarter* 1 (1925–1926): 203–232
Also includes a poem by Ernest Walsh entitled "Ernest Heming-way," p. 67 (H33), and a review of *In Our Time* by "E.W." [Ernest Walsh], pp. 319–321 (H33$_2$)

118. "Banal Story"
Short story in *Little Review* 12 (1926): pp. 22–23
c170

119. "The Killers"
Short story in *Scribner's Magazine*, March 1927, pp. 227–233
c172

120. "Nothoemist Poem"

Poem in *Exile*, no. 1 (1927), p. 21
Collected with *Exile*, nos. 2–4 (1927–1928)
C174

121. Another copy each of *Exile*, nos. 1 and 2

122. "An Alpine Idyll"

Short story in *The American Caravan, A Yearbook of American Liter-
ature,* edited by Van Wyck Brooks, Alfred Kreymborg, Lewis
Mumford, and Paul Rosenfeld, pp. 46–51
New York: The Macaulay Company, 1927
Green cloth
B5

123. Another copy

124. *A Farewell to Arms*

Novel in *Scribner's Magazine*, May 1929–October 1929
Bound in one volume, blue cloth
C188

125. "Introduction"

For *Kiki's Memoirs* by Kiki, pp. 9–14
Paris: Edward W. Titus, 1930
Translated by Samuel Putnam
Illustrated by Kiki
Paper covers
B7

126. Another copy

SIGNED: "Samuel Putnam," p. 23

127. "Ultimately"

Poem for *Salmagundi* by William Faulkner, back cover
Milwaukee: The Casanova Press, 1932
Limited special first edition
Number 330 of 525 copies
Preface by Paul Romaine
Paper covers
B11

128. "Introduction"

For *This Must Be the Place: Memoirs of Montparnasse by Jimmie the Barman* (*James Charters*), edited by Morrill Cody, pp. 11–13
London: Herbert Joseph Ltd., 1934
Illustrated by Ivan Opffer and Hilaire Hiler
Blue cloth with dust jacket
B15

129. Commentary

In *Quintanilla*, pp. [2]–[3]
New York: Pierre Matisse Gallery, [1934]
Catalogue of an exhibition of Luis Quintanilla's paintings at the Pierre Matisse Gallery, November 20–December 4, 1934, including an appraisal of Quintanilla's work by Ernest Hemingway
Single sheet folded
B16

130. Commentary

In *Gattorno*, pp. 11–16
Havana: Ucar, Garcia y Cia, 1935
Paper covers
Catalogue of the paintings of Cuban artist Antonio Gattorno, including a commentary on Gattorno's work by Ernest Hemingway
B17

131. "Marlin Off Cuba"

Article in *American Big Game Fishing*, edited by Eugene V. Connett, pp. 55–81
New York: The Derrydale Press, 1935
Illustrated by Lynn Bogue Hunt
Blue cloth
B18

132. "Notes on the Next War"

Article in *American Points of View: A Reader's Guide, 1935*, edited by William H. Cordell and Kathryn Coe Cordell, pp. 1–8
Garden City, New York: Doubleday, Doran & Company, 1936
Black cloth with dust jacket
E54

133. "The Malady of Power"

Article in *American Points of View 1936*, edited by William H. Cordell and Kathryn Coe Cordell, pp. 184–191
Garden City, New York: Doubleday, Doran & Company, 1937
Black cloth with dust jacket
B22

134. "The Snows of Kilimanjaro"

Short story in *The Best Short Stories 1937 and the Yearbook of the American Short Story*, edited by Edward J. O'Brien, pp. 105–126
Boston and New York: Houghton Mifflin Company, 1937
Red cloth with dust jacket
B24

135. "On the Blue Water: A Gulf Stream Letter"

Article in *Blow the Man Down: The Yachtsman's Reader*, edited by Eric Devine, pp. 304–311
Garden City, New York: Doubleday, Doran & Company, 1937
Blue cloth
B25

136. "The Writer and War"

Paper in *The Writer in a Changing World*, edited by Henry Hart, pp. 69–73
[New York]: Equinox Cooperative Press, 1937
Beige cloth with dust jacket
B26

137. Telegram and statement

In *Writers Take Sides: Letters About the War in Spain from 418 American Authors*, pp. [viii], 30
New York: The League of American Writers, 1938
Paper covers
B29
Telegram from Paris, April 1, [1938], signed by Ernest Hemingway, Vincent Sheen, and Louis Fischer (p. [viii]); statement (p. 30)

138. Another copy

139. "The Spanish War"

NANA dispatches reprinted in *Fact* (London), no. 16 (1938), pp.
   7–72
Sup C18

140. Another copy

141. "Milton Wolff"

Article in *Jo Davidson: Spanish Portraits*, p. [25]
New York: The Georgian Press, [1939]
Paper covers
B31
Reissued catalogue, probably for an exhibition of Jo Davidson's
   work at the Whyte Gallery in Washington, D.C., January 5–18,
   1939, including accompanying text for Milton Wolff bust by
   Ernest Hemingway

142. Another copy

143. "Foreword"

For *Men in the Ranks: The Story of 12 Americans in Spain* by Joseph
   North, pp. 3–4
[New York: Friends of the Abraham Lincoln Brigade, 1939]
Paper covers
B33

144. "Preface"

For *All the Brave* by Luis Quintanilla, pp. 7–11
New York: Modern Age Books, 1939
Text by Elliot Paul and Jay Allen
Trade edition
Paper covers
B34

145. Another copy

146. "From a Medieval Chronicle"

Thirteen-line epigraph in *A Stricken Field* by Martha Gellhorn,
   p. [vii]
New York: Duell, Sloan and Pearce, 1940
Beige cloth
B36

147. "Preface"

For *The Great Crusade* by Gustav Regler, pp. vii–xi
New York and Toronto: Longmans, Green and Company, 1940
Translated by Whittaker Chambers and Barrows Mussey
Red cloth with dust jacket
B38

148. "Preface"

For *The Great Crusade* by Gustav Regler, pp. [5]–[9]
New York and Toronto: Longmans, Green and Company, 1940
Translated by Whittaker Chambers and Barrows Mussey
Sixteen-page promotional leaflet including Hemingway's preface
    in full
Unbound with dust jacket
B38

149. "Introduction"

For *Studio: Europe* by John Groth, pp. 7–9
New York: The Vanguard Press, 1945
Illustrated by the author
Blue cloth with dust jacket
B43

150. Another copy

Signed by the author

151. "Introduction"

For *Treasury for the Free World*, edited by Ben Raeburn, pp. xiii–xv
New York: Arco Publishing Company, 1946
Grey cloth with dust jacket
B44

152. "Introduction"

For *In Sicily* by Elio Vittorini, pp. [7]–[8]
New York: A New Directions Book, 1949
Translated by Wilfrid David
Yellow cloth with dust jacket
B48

153. Another copy

154. Commentary

In *Reginald Rowe*, p. [3]

New York: Wellons Gallery, 1952

Catalogue of an exhibition of Reginald Rowe's paintings at the
    Wellons Gallery, February 18–March 1, 1952, including an
    appraisal of Rowe's work by Ernest Hemingway

Single sheet folded

B52

155. *The Old Man and the Sea*

[*Life*, September 1, 1952]

Galley proofs of novel

156. *The Old Man and the Sea*

Novel in *Life*, September 1, 1952, pp. 35–54

C370

157. "Foreword"

For *Man and Beast in Africa* by François Sommer, pp. 5–7

London: Herbert Jenkins, 1953

First English edition

Translated by Edward Fitzgerald

Blue cloth with dust jacket

B50

158. "Preface"

For *Salt Water Fishing* by Van Campen Heilner, pp. vii–viii

New York: Alfred A. Knopf, 1953

Second edition revised

Color paintings and line drawings by W. Goadby Lawrence

Blue and grey cloth with dust jacket

B54

159. "Safari"

Article in *Look*, January 26, 1954, pp. 19–34

C379

160. "Foreword"

For *A Fly Fisher's Life* by Charles Ritz, p. 7

London: Max Reinhardt, 1959

First English edition
Translated by Humphrey Hare
Introduction by Bernard Venables
Blue cloth with dust jacket

161. "The Dangerous Summer" [Part I]
Article in *Life*, September 5, 1960, pp. 78–109
c407

162. Another copy

163. "The Dangerous Summer"—Part II: "The Pride of the Devil"
Article in *Life*, September 12, 1960, pp. 60–82
c407

164. "On the Blue Water: A Gulf Stream Letter"
Article reprinted in *Esquire*, October 1973, p. 141
Sup c79

164a. "The Snows of Kilimanjaro"
Short story reprinted, *Ibid.*, p. 143
Sup c79₁

165. Collaboration
For *Hokum, A Play in Three Acts* by Morris McNeil [Musselman]
    and apparently Ernest Hemingway
Wellesley Hills, Massachusetts: Sans Courci Press, 1979
Number 73 of 73 copies
Introduction by William and Dorothy Young
White cloth with dust jacket, green slipcase

166. "The Unpublished Opening of *The Sun Also Rises*
Article in *Antaeus*, no. 33 (1979), pp. 7–14

PART I:C

TRANSLATIONS

Listed alphabetically by language

---

167. *al-Shaykh wa-al-baḥr wa Thulūj Kilīmānjārū*
(*The Old Man and the Sea* and "The Snows of Kilimanjaro")
Beirut: Dār al-Taḥrīr, 1961
Translated into Arabic by Munīr al-Baʻlabakkī
Paper covers

168. *Farvel til våbnene*
(*A Farewell to Arms*)
Copenhagen: J. H. Schultz, 1936
Translated into Danish by Ole Restrup
Paper covers
D30

169. *At have og ikke have*
(*To Have and Have Not*)
Copenhagen: J. H. Schultz, 1937
Translated into Danish by Ole Restrup
Paper covers
D31

170. *Efter stormem*
("After the Storm" and fifteen other short stories)
Copenhagen: J. H. Schultz, 1942
Translated into Danish by Sigvard Lund
Introduction by Niels Kaas Johansen
Paper covers
D34

171. *De ubesejrede*
("The Undefeated" and thirteen other short stories)

Copenhagen: J. H. Schultz, 1942
Translated into Danish by Sigvard Lund
Introduction by Niels Kaas Johansen
Paper covers
D35

172. *Afrikas gronne bjerge*
(*Green Hills of Africa*)
Copenhagen: J. H. Schultz, 1945
Translated into Danish by Ole Restrup
Paper covers
D39

173. *Over floden — ind i skovene*
(*Across the River and Into the Trees*)
Copenhagen: J. H. Schultz, 1951
Translated into Danish by Georg Gjedde
Paper covers
D41

174. *Den gamle mand og havet*
(*The Old Man and the Sea*)
Copenhagen: J. H. Schultz, 1952
Translated into Danish by Ole Restrup
Paper covers
D42

175. *Sov sødt, mine herrer*
("God Rest You Merry Gentlemen" and thirteen other short
stories)
Copenhagen: J. H. Schultz, 1955
Translated into Danish by Ole Restrup
Paper covers
D43

176. *Cinquante mille dollars*
("Fifty Grand" and five other short stories)
Paris: Éditions de la Nouvelle Revue Française, 1928
Translated into French by Georges Duplaix [Ott de Weymer]
Number XL of 110 copies
Paper covers with dust jacket
D69

177. *Cinquante mille dollars*
("Fifty Grand" and five other short stories)
Paris: Librairie Gallimard, 1928
Translated into French by Georges Duplaix [Ott de Weymer]
Number 365 of 780 copies
Paper covers
D69

178. *Cinquante mille dollars*
("Fifty Grand" and five other short stories)
Paris: Livre de Poche, 1958
Translated into French by Georges Duplaix [Ott de Weymer]
Paper covers
D69, Hanneman dates this edition 1962

179. *L'adieu aux armes*
(*A Farewell to Arms*)
Paris: Librairie Gallimard, 1931
Translated into French by Maurice E. Coindreau
Preface by Drieu la Rochelle
Number 827 of 1180 copies
Paper covers
D70, Hanneman dates this edition 1932

180. *En avoir ou pas*
(*To Have and Have Not*)
Paris: Éditions Gallimard, 1945
Translated into French by Marcel Duhamel
Number XXII of 110 copies
Paper covers with dust jacket
D75

181. *Dix indiens*
("Ten Indians" and eleven other short stories)
Paris: Librairie Gallimard, 1946
Translated into French by Marcel Duhamel
Number XXXVIII of 105 copies
Paper covers
D76

182. *Paradis perdu suivi de La cinquième colonne*
(Thirty-one short stories and *The Fifth Column*)

Paris: Librairie Gallimard, 1949
Translated into French by Henri Robillot and Marcel Duhamel
Number 9 of 205 copies
Paper covers with dust jacket
D77

183. Another copy
Number 116 of 205 copies

184. Another copy
Unnumbered
Variant binding

185. *Paris est une fête*
(*A Moveable Feast*)
Paris: Éditions Gallimard, 1964
Translated into French by Marc Saporta
Preface by the author
Unnumbered copy, edition of 112 numbered copies
Paper covers
D85

186. *Les neiges du Kilimandjaro*
("The Snows of Kilimanjaro" and three other short stories)
Lausanne: La Petite Ourse, 1966
Translated into French by Marcel Duhamel
Brown leather

187. *En ligne*
(*By-Line; Ernest Hemingway*)
Paris: Éditions Gallimard, 1970
Translated into French by Jean-René Major and Georges Magnane
Number 30 of 52 copies
Paper covers
Sup D35

188. *Wem die Stunde schlägt*
(*For Whom the Bell Tolls*)
Berlin: Suhrkamp Verlag, 1948

Translated into German by Paul Baudisch
Paper covers with dust jacket
D91, variant pagination; Hanneman states 544 pp., this copy has
424 pp.

189. *O jeros kai i Thalassa*
(*The Old Man and the Sea*)
Athens: Icaros, [1954]
Translated into Greek by D. Berachas
Paper covers with dust jacket
D119

190. *Wezarah hashemesh*
(*The Sun Also Rises*)
Tel Aviv: Am Ovid Publishers, 1973
Translated into Hebrew by Wera Israelit
Paper covers
D129
Later edition of Hanneman entry

191. *Morte nel pomeriggio*
(*Death in the Afternoon*)
Milan: Arnoldo Mondadori, [1962]
Translated into Italian by Fernanda Pivano
Prefatory note by the author
Paper covers
D166

192. *Addio alle armi*
(*A Farewell to Arms*)
Milan: Arnoldo Mondadori, 1961
Translated into Italian by Fernanda Pivano
Introduction by the author
Green cloth with dust jacket

193. *Den ene mot de mange*
(*To Have and Have Not*)
Oslo: Glydendal Norsk Forlag, 1938
Translated into Norwegian by Gunnar Larsen
Foreword by Sigurd Hoel

INSCRIBED: "To Mr. and Mrs. Alvin C. Hamer very gratefully
Ernest Hemingway Hope you can read this. I can't."
Paper covers with dust jacket
D234

194. *Śniegi Kilimandżaro i inne opowiadania*
("The Snows of Kilimanjaro" and twenty-two other short stories)
Warsaw: Państwowy Instytut Wydawniczy, 1956
Translated into Polish by Mira Michalowska, Jan Zakrzewski,
and Bronislaw Zieliński
Foreword by Bronislaw Zieliński
Paper covers
D254, variant pagination; Hanneman states 349 pp., this copy
has 336 pp.

195. *Zelenye kholmy Afriki*
(*Green Hills of Africa*)
Moscow: Geografgiz, 1959
Translated into Russian by V. A. Khinkis
Paper covers
D297

196. *Proshchai oruzhie!*
(*A Farewell to Arms*)
Moscow: Gosudarstvennoe Izdatelśtvo Khudozhestvennoi litera-
tury
Translated into Russian by M. Urnova
Foreword by M. Urnova
Paper covers
D300

197. *Adiós a las armas*
(*A Farewell to Arms*)
Barcelona: Luis de Caralt, 1957
Translated into Spanish by Joana M. Vda. Horta and Joaquim
Horta
Green cloth with dust jacket
D322

198. *Las verdes colinas de Africa*
(*Green Hills of Africa*)
Barcelona: Luis de Caralt, 1964

Orange cloth with dust jacket
Sup D117

199. *El viejo y el mar*
(*The Old Man and the Sea*)
Barcelona: Editorial Planeta, 1969
Translated into Spanish by Lino Novás Calvo
Brown cloth with dust jacket

200. *El viejo y el mar*
(*The Old Man and the Sea*)
Mexico City: Editores Mexicanos Unidos, 1976
Translated into Spanish by Lino Novás Calvo
Paper covers

201. *Farväl till vapnen*
(*A Farewell to Arms*)
Stockholm: Albert Bonniers Forlag, 1943
Translated into Swedish by Louis Renner
Introduction by Sten Selander
Brown cloth

202. *sànǎam chiiwíd*
("The Short Happy Life of Francis Macomber" and nine other
short stories)
Bangkok: Ruam Sarn, 1969
Translated into Thai by Asa Khochitmet
Blue cloth with dust jacket

PART I:D

ADAPTATIONS

---

203. *For Whom the Bell Tolls*
   Hollywood: Paramount Pictures, July 20, 1942
   Screenplay by Dudley Nichols
   SIGNED: "Gary Cooper, Ingrid Bergman, Sam Wood, Artura de
   Cordova, Akim Tamiroff, Katina Paxinov"

204. "The Killers"
   Universal City: Mark Hellinger Productions, April 3, 1946
   Screenplay by Anthony Veiller

205. "The Snows of Kilimanjaro"
   Hollywood: Twentieth Century Fox, March 28, 1951
   Screenplay by Casey Robinson
   INITIALLED: "DZ" [Darryl Zanuck]

206. *The Old Man and the Sea*
   French subtitles and technical continuity material
   Hollywood: Warner Brothers, 1958
   Subtitles by Jean Aron

207. *Two Stories*
   ("Fifty Grand" and "The Undefeated")
   Copenhagen: Grafisk Forlag AS, 1968
   Adaptation for children, illustrated by Oskar Jørgensen
   Paper covers

208. *Islands in the Stream*
   Hollywood: Paramount Pictures, September 10, 1975
   Screenplay by Denne Bart Petitclerc

PART I:E

EPHEMERA

---

209. *Bibliographical Notes on Ernest Hemingway*

Excerpted "from a Hemingway letter [dated Spring 1927] in answer to questions concerning editions and number of copies"

Printed October 1930 by The Walden Book Shop, Chicago

SIGNED: "Ernest Hemingway"

Single sheet folded

210. Bastard note

Facsimile of the proof sheet of the legal disclaimer on p. [x] of the second printing of *A Farewell to Arms* in 1929

93 copies printed, December 1931, by Louis Henry Cohn

1 p.

F150

211. *Ciao*

Facsimile of *Ciao* (June 1918), the monthly newspaper published by the American Red Cross ambulance unit, Section IV, in Vicenza, Italy, including "Al Receives Another Letter" by Ernest Hemingway

200 copies printed as a Keepsake, n.d., by Matthew J. Bruccoli to commemorate the first exhibition from the Joseph M. Bruccoli Great War Collection, Alderman Library, The University of Virginia

4 pp.

Sup F168

212. "Les seuls gens bien du Canada"

Reprint of letter from Ernest Hemingway to Sylvia Beach, Toronto, November 6, 1923

500 copies printed as a Keepsake in Toronto, May 1969, in matching French and English editions

Single sheet folded

213. "The Only Nice People in Canada"

Reprint of letter from Ernest Hemingway to Sylvia Beach, Toronto, November 6, 1923

500 copies printed as a Keepsake in Toronto, May 1969, in matching French and English editions

Single sheet folded

214. From *Cooperative Commonwealth*

Facsimile of three pages of the *Co-operative Commonwealth*, II, iv (December 1920), including "Will You Let These Kiddies Miss Santa Claus?" by Ernest Hemingway

Number 94 of 125 copies printed as a Keepsake for Friends of the *Fitzgerald/Hemingway Annual* in December 1970 by Matthew J. Bruccoli and C. E. Frazer Clark, Jr.

INITIALLED: "CEFC" [C. E. Frazer Clark, Jr.] and "MJB" [Matthew J. Bruccoli]

INSCRIBED: "For Bill Rayburn's great Hemingway collection" [C. E. Frazer Clark, Jr.]

4 pp.

Sup F171

215. From *Trapeze*

Facsimile of page one of the *Trapeze*, VI (November 3, 1916), partially including Ernest Hemingway's article "Athletic Association to Organize Next Week"

Number 48 of 150 copies printed as a Keepsake for distribution at the Chicago Hemingway Conference, December 28, 1971, to Friends of the *Fitzgerald/Hemingway Annual*

Single sheet folded

Sup F172

216. Dust jacket

For *Revolution in Cuba; An Essay in Understanding* by Herbert L. Matthews

New York: Charles Scribner's Sons, 1975

Blurb on back cover reads: "And when the fakers are all dead they will read Matthews in the schools to find out what really happened. Ernest Hemingway"

PART II

Writings about Hemingway

A.
BOOKS AND PAMPHLETS ABOUT HEMINGWAY

B.
NEWSPAPER, PERIODICAL AND
EPHEMERAL MATERIAL ABOUT HEMINGWAY

PART II:A

BOOKS & PAMPHLETS ABOUT HEMINGWAY

---

217. Arnold, Lloyd
    Hemingway: High on the Wild
    New York: Grosset & Dunlap, 1977
    Foreword by John H. Hemingway
    Blue cloth with dust jacket

218. Another copy

219. Aronowitz, Alfred G. and Hamill, Peter
    Ernest Hemingway: The Life and Death of a Man
    New York: Lancer Books, 1961
    Paper covers
    G18

220. Atkins, John
    The Art of Ernest Hemingway: His Work and Personality
    London: Spring Books, 1964
    Revised edition
    Preface by the author
    Tan cloth with dust jacket
    G22(b)

221. Baker, Carlos
    Ernest Hemingway: A Life Story
    New York: Charles Scribner's Sons, 1969
    Blue cloth with dust jacket
    Sup B10

222. Baker, Carlos, ed.
    Ernest Hemingway: Selected Letters, 1917–1961
    New York: Charles Scribner's Sons, 1981
    Number 202 of 500 copies, signed by the editor
    White and brown cloth with dust jacket, brown slipcase

223. Bruccoli, Matthew J. *et al.*, eds.

Fitzgerald/Hemingway Annual

Washington, D.C.: NCR/Microcard Editions 1969–1973; Englewood, Colorado: Information Handling Service, 1975–1976; Detroit: Gale Research, 1977

Inscribed for Toby Holtzman by co-editor C. E. Frazer Clark, Jr.

Various cloth bindings

224. Bruccoli, Matthew J.

Scott and Ernest: The Authority of Failure and the Authority of Success

[New York: Random House, 1978]

Galley proofs

225. Bruccoli, Matthew J.

Scott and Ernest: The Authority of Failure and the Authority of Success

New York: Random House, 1978

Brown and rust cloth with dust jacket

226. [Bruccoli, Matthew J. and Clark, C. E. Frazer, Jr.]

F. Scott Fitzgerald and Ernest M. Hemingway in Paris

Bloomfield Hills, Michigan and Columbia, South Carolina: Bruccoli-Clark, 1972

Catalogue of an exhibition at the Bibliothèque Benjamin Franklin in Paris, June 23–24, 1972, in conjunction with a conference at the Institut d'Études Américaines

Paper covers

Sup G57

227. [Bruccoli, Matthew J. and Clark, C. E. Frazer, Jr.]

In Their Time/1920–1940

Bloomfield Hills, Michigan and Columbia, South Carolina: Bruccoli-Clark, 1977

Foreword by Honoria Murphy Donnelly

Catalogue of an exhibition at the University of Virginia Library, December 1977–March 1978

Paper covers

228. Buckley, Peter

Ernest

New York: The Dial Press, 1978

Black cloth with dust jacket

229. Burgess, Anthony
Ernest Hemingway and His World
New York: Charles Scribner's Sons, 1978
Green cloth with dust jacket

230. Carlisle, Harry, ed.
The Legacy of Abner Green: A Memorial Journal
New York: American Committee for the Protection of the Foreign
   Born, 1959
Paper covers
Sup G67

231. Castillo-Puche, Jose Luis
Hemingway in Spain
New York: Doubleday & Company, 1974
Translated by Helen R. Lane
Black cloth with dust jacket

232. [Clark, C. E. Frazer, Jr.]
Ernest M. Hemingway: The Paris Years . . . and Before
Farmington, Michigan: Oakland Community College, 1973
Catalogue of an exhibition at the Oakland Community College,
   May 2, 1973, in conjunction with the Library Technical As-
   sistance Citizens Advisory Committee
Single sheet folded
Sup G79

233. Cohn, Louis Henry
A Bibliography of the Works of Ernest Hemingway
New York: Random House, 1931
Number 40 of 505 copies
INSCRIBED: "Dear Dr. Guffey: If all these first editions that I
   have signed for you are worth only ½ of what you paid for them
   —and I don't say they are—then I must have done about 1500
   dollars worth of inscription, anecdote and libel writing in them
   —But here I am at 10 o'clock at night still inscribing Capt.
   Cohn's volume—and very glad to for you—but I'll be damned
   if I would for anyone else—Ernest Hemingway"
Black cloth
B9

234. Connolly, Cyril
The Unquiet Grave
London: Hamish Hamilton, 1945
SIGNED: "Hemingway"
Grey cloth

235. Davidson, Bill
Cut Off
New York: Stein and Day, 1972
INSCRIBED: "To George Seaton with admiration Bill Davidson"
Green and red cloth with dust jacket

236. Donaldson, Scott
By Force of Will: The Life and Art of Ernest Hemingway
New York: The Viking Press, 1977
White and red cloth with dust jacket

237. [Goodwin, Jonathan]
*Important Modern First Editions, With Autograph Letters and Manu-
scripts of Ernest Hemingway and Others*
New York: Sotheby Parke-Bernet, 1977
Paper covers

238. Grieg, Harald
På fisketur med Hemingway
(On a Fishing Trip with Hemingway)
Oslo: Privately printed, 1951
Inscribed in Danish
Paper covers
G170

239. [Guffey, Don Carlos]
*First Editions of English and American Authors: The Library of Dr. Don
Carlos Guffey*
New York: Parke-Bernet Galleries, 1958
Paper covers
G174

240. Hanneman, Audre
Ernest Hemingway: A Comprehensive Bibliography
Princeton, New Jersey: Princeton University Press, 1967

Foreword by Charles Scribner, Jr.
Tan cloth with dust jacket
Sup G178

241. Harmon, Robert B.
The First Editions of Ernest Hemingway
Los Altos, California: Hermes Publications, 1978
Paper covers

242. Heimburg, Carol
Etched Portraits of Ernest Hemingway
Northampton, Massachusetts: Apiary Press, 1961
Number 44 of 50 copies, signed by the artist
Blue cloth
G184

243. Heiney, Donald
Barron's Simplified Approach to Ernest Hemingway
Woodbury, New York: Barron's Educational Series, 1965
Paper covers
G185

244. Hemingway, Gregory H.
Papa: A Personal Memoir
Boston: Houghton Mifflin Company, 1976
Preface by Norman Mailer
Black and brown cloth with dust jacket

245. Another copy

246. Hemingway, Leicester
The Sound of the Trumpet
New York: Henry Holt, 1953
Tan and blue cloth with dust jacket

247. Hemingway, Mary Welsh
How it Was
New York: Alfred A. Knopf, 1976
Black cloth with dust jacket

248. Another copy
Inscribed: "For the Holtzman family library Mary Hemingway
2-16-1977"

249. Herrmann, Lazar [Leo Lania]

Hemingway: A Pictorial Biography
New York: The Viking Press, 1961
First English edition
Translated by Joan Bradley
Grey cloth with dust jacket
G226(a)

250. Herrmann, Lazar [Leo Lania]

Hemingway: A Pictorial Biography
New York: The Viking Press, 1961
First English edition, second printing
Translated by Joan Bradley
Grey cloth with dust jacket
G226(a)

251. Hotchner, A. E.

Papa Hemingway: A Personal Memoir
New York: Random House, 1966
Black and brown cloth with dust jacket
G198

252. Another copy

253. Hotchner, A. E.

Papa Hemingway: The Ecstasy and Sorrow
New York: Quill, William Morrow and Company, 1983
Paper covers

254. Isabelle, Julanne

Hemingway's Religious Experience
New York: Chip's Bookshop Booksellers and Publishers, 1964
Beige cloth

255. Johnson, Merle

Merle Johnson's American First Editions
New York: R. R. Bowker Company, 1947
Fourth edition
Revised and enlarged by Jacob Blanck
Red cloth

256. Kiley, Jed
Hemingway: An Old Friend Remembers
New York: Hawthorn Books, 1965
Brown cloth
G214

257. Another copy
Brown cloth with dust jacket

258. Kiley, Jed
Hemingway: A Title Fight in Ten Rounds
London: Methuen, 1965
Published in the United States under the title *Hemingway: An Old Friend Remembers*
Brown cloth with dust jacket
G214

259. Klimo, Vernon (Jake) and Oursler, Will
Hemingway and Jake: An Extraordinary Friendship
Garden City, New York: Doubleday & Company, 1972
Blue and grey cloth with dust jacket
Sup G233

260. Kvam, Wayne E.
Hemingway in Germany: The Fiction, the Legend and the Critics
Athens, Ohio: Ohio University Press, 1973
Brown cloth with dust jacket
Sup G242

261. Laurence, Frank M.
Hemingway and the Movies
Jackson: University Press of Mississippi, 1981
Green cloth with dust jacket

262. Levidova, Nina Mikhailovna and Parchevskaia, B. M.
Ernest Khemingueĭ: Bio-bibliograficeskij ukazatel
(Ernest Hemingway Bibliography)
Moscow: Kniga, 1970
Preface by N. M. Levidova
Paper covers
Sup G254

263. McCaffery, John K. M., ed.
Ernest Hemingway: The Man and His Work
Cleveland and New York: The World Publishing Company, 1950
Grey cloth with dust jacket
G255

264. Machlin, Milt
The Private Hell of Hemingway
New York: Paperback Library, 1962
Paper covers
G260

265. McLendon, James
Papa: Hemingway in Key West
Miami, Florida: E. A. Seemann, 1972
Advance copy
Unbound with dust jacket
Sup G277

266. Miller, Madelaine Hemingway
Ernie: Hemingway's Sister "Sunny" Remembers
New York: Crown Publishers, 1975
Preface by Robert Traver
White and red cloth with dust jacket

267. Another copy

268. Montgomery, Constance Cappel
Hemingway in Michigan
New York: Fleet Publishing, 1966
Brown and black cloth with dust jacket
B61

269. Montgomery, Constance Cappel
Hemingway in Michigan
Waitsfield, Vermont: Vermont Crossroads Press, 1977
Paperback edition

270. [Nobel Foundation and the Swedish Academy]
Les Prix Nobel en 1954
(Program of the Nobel Prize Awards)

Stockholm: Imprimerie Royale P.A. Norstedt & Söner, 1955
Paper covers
B56

271. [Nobel Foundation and the Swedish Academy]
Nobel Prize Library: Ernest Hemingway Knut Hamsun Hermann Hesse
New York: Alexis Gregory; Del Mar, California: CRM Publishing, 1971
Blue leather
Sup G315

272. Nolan, William F.
Hemingway: Last Days of the Lion
Santa Barbara, California: Capra Press, 1974
Privately printed, limited edition
Number 12 of 75 copies, signed by the author
Red and grey boards

273. Another copy
Unnumbered
Paper covers

274. Phillips, Gene D.
Hemingway and Film
New York: Frederick Ungar, 1980
Paper covers

275. Randall, David A.
Dukedom Large Enough
New York: Random House, 1969
Signed by the author
Red cloth with dust jacket
Sup G343

276. Rodman, Maia
The People in His Life
New York: Stein and Day, 1980
Black and beige cloth with dust jacket

277. Ross, Lillian
Portrait of Hemingway
New York: Simon & Schuster, 1961

Brown and yellow cloth with dust jacket
G342

278. Samuels, Lee
A Hemingway Check List
New York: Charles Scribner's Sons, 1951
Preface by Ernest Hemingway
Blue cloth with dust jacket
B51

279. Sanderson, Stewart F.
Ernest Hemingway
Edinburgh and London: Oliver & Boyd, 1961
Paper covers
G349

280. Sanderson, Stewart F.
Ernest Hemingway
New York: Grove Press, 1961
First American edition
Paper covers
G349

281. Sarason, Bertram D.
Hemingway and the Sun Set
Washington, D.C.: NCR/Microcard Editions, 1972
Red cloth with dust jacket
Sup G363

282. Seward, William
My Friend Ernest Hemingway: An Affectionate Reminiscence
South Brunswick and New York: A. S. Barnes; London: Thomas
    Yoseloff, 1969
Purple cloth with dust jacket
Sup G376

283. Singer, Kurt
Hemingway: Life and Death of a Giant
Los Angeles: Holloway House, 1961
Illustrated by Ben Kudo
Paper covers
G374

284. Stephens, Robert O.
Hemingway's Nonfiction: The Public Voice
Chapel Hill: University of North Carolina Press, 1968
Red cloth with dust jacket
Sup G388

285. Weeks, Robert P., ed.
Hemingway: A Collection of Critical Essays
Englewood Cliffs, New Jersey: Prentice-Hall, 1962
Black cloth with dust jacket
G439

286. White, William
Ernest Hemingway (21 July 1899–2 July 1961) Guide to a Memorial Exhibition
Detroit: University of Detroit Library, 1961
Catalogue of an exhibition at the University of Detroit Library, July 14–August 12, 1961
Single sheet folded
G445

287. White, William, ed.
The Merrill Studies in "The Sun Also Rises"
Columbus, Ohio: Charles E. Merrill, 1969
INSCRIBED: "For the Holtzman Family Library with the editor's regards Wm. White Detroit 10 December 1969"
Paper covers
Sup G432

288. White, William
The Merrill Guide to Ernest Hemingway
Columbus, Ohio: Charles E. Merrill, 1969
INSCRIBED: "For Toby Book Club Auction Night, 10 December 1969 Regards, Bill White"
Paper covers
Sup G433

289. Young, Philip
Ernest Hemingway
New York and Toronto: Rinehart & Company, 1952
Tan cloth with dust jacket
G460

290. Young, Philip
Ernest Hemingway
Minneapolis: University of Minnesota Press, 1959
Paper covers
G461

291. Young, Philip and Mann, Charles W.
The Hemingway Manuscripts: An Inventory
University Park and London: Pennsylvania State University
   Press, 1969
Beige cloth and brown leather, grey slipcase
Sup BI1

PART II:B

NEWSPAPER, PERIODICAL & EPHEMERAL

MATERIAL ABOUT HEMINGWAY

---

292. "Ernest Hemingway"
     By Lawrence H. Conrad
     In *Landmark* 16 (1934): 397–400
     H245

293. "'And stories end . . .'"
     In *Time*, October 18, 1937, pp. 79–85
     Cover story and review of *To Have and Have Not*
     H336

294. "Hemingway in Italy"
     By Mario Praz
     In *Partisan Review* 15 (1948): 1086–1100
     H591

295. "The Author's Name Is Hemingway"
     By John O'Hara
     In *New York Times Book Review*, September 10, 1950, p. 1
     Review of *Across the River and Into the Trees*
     H643

296. "The Art of Fiction, XXI: Ernest Hemingway"
     By George Plimpton
     In *Paris Review* 5 (1958): 60–89
     H1066

297. "A Reunion in Death"
     In *San Francisco Chronicle*, July 5, 1961, p. 26

298. "Hemingway's Funeral Today"
     In *San Francisco Chronicle*, July 5, 1961
     Dateline: Ketchum, Idaho

299. "A Simple Burial for Hemingway"
     In *San Francisco Chronicle*, July 6, 1961
     Dateline: Ketchum, Idaho

300. "Hemingway Was 'Just Like a Ghost' "
     In *San Francisco Chronicle*, July 10, 1961
     Dateline: Minneapolis

301. "Our Warmest Memories of Hemingway"
     In *Life*, July 14, 1961, p. 2
     HI274

301a. "Hemingway: Driving Force of a Great Artist"
     Ibid., pp. 59–69
     Photographic essay
     HI274₁

301b. "His Mirror Was Danger"
     By Archibald MacLeish
     Ibid., pp. 71–72
     HI274₂

302. "Hemingway"
     By Ilya Ehrenburg
     In *Soviet Review* 3 (1962): 22–26
     HI421

303. "Letters of Ernest Hemingway to Soviet Writers"
     By Ivan Kashkeen
     In *Soviet Literature*, no. 11 (1962), pp. 158–167
     HI427

304. "Jack Hemingway of Mill Valley: How He
     Remembers 'Papa' "
     In *San Francisco Examiner*, "Pictorial Living," November 4, 1962,
     pp. 14–18

305 "Letters from Hemingway"
In *San Francisco Examiner*, "The American Weekly," May 12, 1963,
    pp. 1-4

306. "Letters from Hemingway"
By Carlos Baker
In *Princeton University Library Chronicle* 24 (1963): 101-107
H1484

307. "What Is Hemingway's Style"
By Ivan Kashkeen
In *Soviet Literature*, no. 6 (1964), pp. 172-180
H1497

308. "Hemingway's Old Cuban Home"
In *San Francisco Chronicle*, June 14, 1964, p. 13
Dateline: San Francisco de Paula, Cuba

309. "Encounter with Hemingway"
By Hugo Gernsback
In *Sexology*, November 1964, pp. 224-225

310. "The Dashes in Hemingway's *A Farewell to Arms*"
By James B. Meriwether
In *Papers of the Bibliographical Society of America* 58 (1964): 449-457
H1557

311. "Papa Hemingway"
By A. E. Hotchner
In *Saturday Evening Post*, April 9, 1966, p. 34
Sup H195
Conclusion of three-part serialization of Hotchner's *Papa Heming-
    way: A Personal Memoir* (No. 251)

312. "Hemingway as Reporter: An Unknown News
    Story"
By William White
In *Journalism Quarterly* 43 (1966): 538-542
Sup H261

313. **"A Soviet Critic's View on Hemingway"**
By Elena Gousseva
In *Soviet Literature*, no. 8 (1967), pp. 172–178
Review of *Ernest Hemingway: A Critico-Biographical Study* by Ivan
    Kashkeen

314. **"Joe: He's a Character Fit for Hemingway"**
By Tom Dammann
In *The Detroit News*, March 29, 1972, p. 12A
Dateline: Harbor Springs, Michigan

315. **"Hemingway's Pal, Joe Bacon, Dies"**
[Detroit], October 1, 1972
Dateline: Petoskey, Michigan

316. **"Hemingway: The Best of What He Had"**
By Michael Murphy
In *The American Way*, July 1974, pp. 11–14

317. **"Hemingway's Movable Feast: Paris' Left Bank
    Revisited"**
By James Morgan
In *TWA Ambassador*, September 1974, pp. 8–10

318. **Column excerpt on Mary Hemingway**
[Detroit], January 30, 1975

319. **"How to Improve Hemingway (Moscow Style)"**
By Jules Telesin
In *Encounter* 46 (1976): 81–86

320. **"Rolf Hochhuth Probes Hemingway's Fate"**
By Fritz L. Raddatz
In *San Francisco Sunday Examiner and Chronicle*, "Datebook," July 11,
    1976

321. **"Court's Harsh Review"**
In *San Francisco Chronicle*, August 4, 1976, p. 26
Dateline: New York

322. **"Mary Hemingway's Years with Ernest"**
By Carlos Baker
In *Saturday Review*, October 2, 1976, pp. 24–27
Review of *How It Was* by Mary Welsh Hemingway (No. 247)

322a. **"The Son Also . . ."**
By Carlos Baker
Ibid., p. 28
Review of *Papa: A Personal Memoir* by Gregory H. Hemingway
(No. 244)

323. **"Man of Short Sentences"**
In *The Daily Telegraph* (England), September 28, 1978

324. **"A Photographic Montage of Hemingway"**
In *San Francisco Sunday Examiner and Chronicle*, December 24, 1978,
p. 43

325. **"Cézanne's Influence on Hemingway"**
By Barnaby Conrad
In *Horizon*, April 1979, pp. 32–37

326. **"Where the Bell Tolled for Hemingway"**
By Jay Clarke
In *San Francisco Sunday Examiner and Chronicle*, July 1, 1979, p. 3

327. **"Ernest Hemingway's Long-Ago Crush on a Vene-
tian Girl Is Once Again the Talk of Italy"**
By Adriana Ivancich von Rex
In *People*, December 1, 1980, pp. 43–44

328. **"American Authors in Paris in the 1920s"**
By Lonnie E. Evans
In *AB Bookman's Weekly*, December 15, 1980, pp. 4011–4016

329. **"Gentlemen's Mail"**
By George Will
In *San Francisco Chronicle*, April 21, 1981

330. "Ernie's Letters Reveal the Man, the Writer"
     In *The Carmel Pine Cone*, May 7, 1981, p. C-2
     Excerpts from *Ernest Hemingway: Selected Letters, 1917–1961* (No.
     222)

331. "Carlos Baker: Deciphering Hemingway"
     By Christopher Sharp
     In *W*, May 8–15, 1981, pp. 12–13

332. "Gabriel García Márquez Meets Ernest Heming-
     way"
     By Gabriel García Márquez
     In *New York Times Book Review*, July 26, 1981, p. 1

333. "Hemingway to Have Bar at the Ritz"
     In [*San Francisco Chronicle*, August 8, 1981, p. 5]
     Dateline: Paris

334. "How Ian Fleming Recruited Me for a Mission to
     Havana"
     By Norman Lewis
     In *Observer Magazine*, November 15, 1981, pp. 63–72

335. "Voyage to Certain Death on Stalin's Orders"
     By Norman Lewis
     In *Observer Magazine*, November 22, 1981, pp. 91–100

336. "The Thriving Hemingway Prose Business"
     By Mike Brumas
     In *San Francisco Examiner*, January 5, 1982, p. E3
     Dateline: New York

337. "Hemingway Bar in Paris"
     By Elizabeth Venant
     In *Travel & Leisure*, February 1982, p. 101

338. "Hemingway's Brother, 67, Kills Himself"
     In *San Francisco Chronicle*, September 15, 1982, p. 38
     Dateline: Miami Beach

339. "Hunt Uncovers 44-Year-Old Hemingway
    Treasure"
    In *San Francisco Sunday Examiner and Chronicle*, November 28, 1982,
    p. A20

340. "How the Story Was Discovered"
    By William B. Watson
    Ibid., p. A21

341. "The FBI's File on Hemingway"
    In *San Francisco Examiner*, October 10, 1983, p. A12
    Dateline: Fort Lauderdale, Florida

342. Review of *The Hemingway Manuscripts: An Inventory*
    by Philip Young and Charles W. Mann
    By Lloyd W. Griggin
    n.p., n.d.

343. Review of filmstrip "Ernest Hemingway the Man:
    A Biographical Interpretation with
    Carlos Baker"
    By Diana Lembo
    n.p., n.d.

344. "Which Writers Will Endure?"
    In [*San Francisco Sunday Examiner and Chronicle*], n.d.

345. Lecture series program
    The Fourth Peters Rushton Seminar in Contemporary Prose and
    Poetry: "Hemingway's Wastelanders" by Carlos Baker, in the
    MacGregor Room of the University of Virginia Library, Char-
    lottesville, March 14, 1952
    Single sheet folded

346. Postcard
    Color photograph of the Ernest Hemingway Home and Museum,
    Key West, Florida
    Produced and printed by John Hinde Ltd., Cabinteely, Co.
    Dublin, Republic of Ireland, n.d.

347. Postcard

Color photograph of the Living Room, Hemingway House, Key West, Florida

No. P303995, produced and printed by Plastichrome, Boston, Massachusetts, n.d.

348. Postcard

Color photograph of the Carriage House Study, Hemingway House, Key West, Florida

No. P303996, produced and printed by Plastichrome, Boston, Massachusetts, n.d.

349. Postcard

Color photograph of the Master Bedroom, Hemingway House, Key West, Florida

No. P303998, produced and printed by Plastichrome, Boston, Massachusetts, n.d.

350. Postcard

Color photograph of the Studio, Hemingway House, Key West, Florida

No. P11151, produced and printed by Dunacolor Graphics Inc., Miami, Florida, n.d.

PART III

Correspondence and Manuscripts

A.
HEMINGWAY CORRESPONDENCE

B.
HEMINGWAY MANUSCRIPTS AND DOCUMENTS

C.
CORRESPONDENCE RELATING TO HEMINGWAY

PART III:A

HEMINGWAY CORRESPONDENCE

---

351. EH to "Tommy" [Thomas G. F. Aitken]

Key West, Florida, March 17, 1936
ALS, 2 pp.
SUMMARY: Fishing stories, and instructions to the editor of *Outdoor Life* regarding publication of EH's reply to a questionnaire on mutilated fish. Praises Aitken's "fine fight for good sportsmanship in fishing," but expresses regret that the only people with the time and money to pursue the sport are "successful business pirates."

352. EH to "Bill" [William Attwood]

Finca Vigia, Cuba, July 10, [19]56
ALS, 2 pp.
SUMMARY: Responds to certain editorial suggestions by *Look* editors, including Attwood who was National Affairs Editor, regarding his article on life in Cuba, (*Look*, September 4, 1956, pp. 23–31). Signed: "Papa." Enclosed is a photocopy of in-house *Look* publication, *Cowles Ink Newsletter*, August 17, 1956, with an item quoting portions of the letter.

353. EH to Carlos Baker

Finca Vigia, Cuba, February 17, 1951
TLS, 3 pp.
SUMMARY: Negative reaction to Princeton professor's proposed critical study, *Hemingway: The Writer As Artist*. Expresses determination "to not aid, and to impede in every way, including legal," any would-be biographer writing during his lifetime. Criticizes Arthur Mizener's biography of F. Scott Fitzgerald.

354. EH to Carlos Baker

Finca Vigia, Cuba, February 24, 1951
ALS, 4 pp.
SUMMARY: Grateful for Baker's agreement to delete biographical

references, noting dissatisfaction with recent profiles by Lillian Ross and Malcolm Cowley (*New Yorker*, May 13, 1950, pp. 36–62; *Life*, January 10, 1949, pp. 86–101). Observes that writing "makes everything else: life, death or green bananas seem completely without importance." Wants Baker to read *The Sea In Being*, later *The Old Man and the Sea*.

355. EH to Carlos Baker

Finca Vigia, Cuba, March 10, 1951
TLS with holograph additions, 2 pp.
SUMMARY: Provides background on the characters and setting of *Across the River and Into the Trees*. At work on the third book of his sea novel, later part of *Islands in the Stream*, which "is . . . like pulling the scab off a wound that was nearly scar tissue." Mentions fishing plans with Air Marshal A. W. Tedder.

356. EH to Carlos Baker

Finca Vigia, Cuba, "Easter Sunday" [March 25, 1951]
TLS, 2 pp.
SUMMARY: Discusses Gertrude Stein's "un generation perdu," with which characterization EH disagrees; ". . . damned if we were lost except for deads, geulle casses and certified crazies." Account of his self-education in languages and literature. Letter of March 10 enclosed.

357. Carlos Baker to EH

Tucson, Arizona, March 26, 1951
TL [carbon], 2 pp. plus questionnaire, 6 pp.
SUMMARY: Queries on early EH publications; literary relations with Sherwood Anderson, Gertrude Stein, Ezra Pound, and Ring Lardner; background on novels; and critical opinions on Joseph Conrad, Mark Twain, Stephen Crane, and Henry James.

358. EH to Carlos Baker

Finca Vigia, Cuba, April 1, 1951
TLS, 6 pp.
SUMMARY: Extensive responses to Baker's "literary questions," with promise to enclose *The Old Man and the Sea* manuscript. Remarks on writing, critics, and reviews, likening the writing of a book to "pitching a one hit game, on a cold and windy day, with a sore arm and in front of empty stands." Further censure of Mizener.

359. EH to Carlos Baker

Finca Vigia, Cuba, April 24, 1951
TLS, 1 p.
SUMMARY: Explains delay in mailing April 1 letter and manuscript of *The Old Man and the Sea*. Describes the "tough metier" of
writing, noting that "nobody can blame Scott Fitzgerald for
quitting . . . so many things were against him and he was always
fragile." Letter of April 1 enclosed.

360. EH to Carlos Baker

Finca Vigia, Cuba, April 29, 1951
TLS, 2 pp.
SUMMARY: Laments the changes in Clark's Fork, Wyoming,
Milan, Valencia, and Oak Park, Illinois. Talk of the critics'
"gang-up" on *Across the River and Into the Trees*, suggesting "a special circle for some of these characters" in Dante's Inferno. Despite
his reputation as a brawler, insists he has "always tried to keep the
obligation *not* to fight in mind," but "nobody ever remembers how
many times you keep your temper."

361. EH to Carlos Baker

Finca Vigia, Cuba, May 9, 1951
TLS with holograph additions, 1 p.
SUMMARY: Response to Baker's factual queries concerning *The
Old Man and the Sea* and reaction to his likening Santiago to King
Lear. "*Lear* is a wonderful play," but "I think the sea was quite old
when Lear was King."

362. EH to Carlos Baker

Finca Vigia, Cuba, June 30, 1951
TLS, 2 pp.
SUMMARY: Pleased, but embarrassed, by Baker's comments on
The Old Man and the Sea and his praise for *The Sun Also Rises* in a
New York Times Book Review article (April 20, 1951, p. 5). Dis-
cussion of Shelley's cremation on the beach at Viarregio, prompted
by Baker's gift of a book of Shelley's poems. Thoughts on his
mother's death.

363. EH to Carlos Baker

Finca Vigia, Cuba, August 27, 1951
ALS, 3 pp.
SUMMARY: Compliments Baker on his *Virginia Quarterly Review*

piece about *A Farewell to Arms* (27 [1951]: 410–418). Rejects suggestion that he review Baker's book prior to publication. Reports "bad luck year" for Hemingways.

364. EH to Carlos Baker

Finca Vigia, Cuba, [P.M. September 4, 1951]
ALS, 3 pp.
SUMMARY: Discusses his mother's "bowdlerized and edited" version of the Hall genealogy and various relatives in a family "more mixed up than Faulkner's." Close friend and Oak Park neighbor Isabel Simmons Godolphin is mentioned. Points out error in *Virginia Quarterly Review* article.

365. EH to Carlos Baker

Finca Vigia, Cuba, October 7, 1951
TLS with holograph additions, 2 pp.
SUMMARY: Suggests changes in Baker's manuscript with regard to his World War I decorations, soldier-friend E. E. Dorman-Smith, and his relationship with Ezra Pound. Comments on Ford Madox Ford, "a great booster of people but a terrible liar," and Gertrude Stein, "her evil genius was Toklas." Hopes Baker's book may "right a few critical wrongs" by journalists who have confused EH's life with his work. Mentions a critical study by New York University professor Philip Young for which he has refused quotation permission.

366. EH to Carlos Baker

Finca Vigia, Cuba, November 2, 1951
TLS, 2 pp.
SUMMARY: Summary of communication with his publisher Charles Scribner, concerning EH's regulation of quotation permission as a means "to control *biography*." Account of his 1944 liberation of Paris' Traveller's Club and Hôtel Ritz with Colonel David Bruce of the OSS. Answers Baker's additional questions about *Across the River and Into the Trees*. Describes events of the past months as "a nightmare of disordered death."

367. EH to Carlos Baker

Finca Vigia, Cuba, November 9, 1951
TLS with holograph additions, 2 pp.
SUMMARY: Reaction to the death of Princeton Dean Christian Gauss, with reminiscences of Paris and Scott Fitzgerald. Discusses

his relationship with Malcolm Cowley, including references to Paris in the twenties and EH's boyhood in Upper Michigan. Offers personal opinions on *The Fifth Column* ("probably the most unsatisfactory thing I ever wrote"), *For Whom the Bell Tolls* ("the best that I can write until this new one"), *Green Hills of Africa*, and *To Have and Have Not*.

368. EH to Carlos Baker

Finca Vigia, Cuba, November 22, 1951
TLS, 1 p.
SUMMARY: Mentions his old-style epigraphs in *Winner Take Nothing* and Martha Gellhorn's *A Stricken Field*, expressing a desire to have lived in those days "before all the books had been written and all the stories told for the first time." More on Paris and Malcolm Cowley.

369. EH to Carlos Baker

Finca Vigia, Cuba, January 14, 1952
TLS, 1 p.
SUMMARY: Reluctantly grants permission to use quotations from his letters to Max Perkins of Scribner's. "Letters are like conversation and I am not careful in either of these ways of communication. . . ." Describes his "complicated relationship" with Marita San Felice, the wife of an Italian diplomat in Cuba and EH's fishing companion.

370. EH to Carlos Baker

Finca Vigia, Cuba, June 4, 1952
TLS, 2 pp.
SUMMARY: Reports anticipated September publication of *The Old Man and the Sea*. Has reconsidered refusal of quotation permission to Philip Young, despite his assertion of EH's "traumatic neurosis" in a paper delivered at a Modern Language Association meeting in Detroit. Questions the ethics of "the two new schools of critics, the amateur detectives and the amateur psychiatrists" and notes that the rudeness necessary to combat their "invasion of privacy" is detrimental to the writer who "should feel what every man feels and especially what your enemies feel." Reference to his father's suicide.

371. EH to Carlos Baker

Finca Vigia, Cuba, August 26, 1952

ALS with holograph additions, 4 pp.

SUMMARY: Thanks Baker for his book, but admits he feels little emotion for it. Discussion of the early years in Paris, particularly his relationship with Alfred Flechtheim, editor of *Der Querschnitt*. Comments on composer George Antheil and writers Samuel Putnam and Ford Madox Ford and the inaccuracy of their reminiscences. Expresses his contempt for Wyndham Lewis.

372. EH to Carlos Baker

Finca Vigia, Cuba, November 3, 1952
TLS, 1 p.

SUMMARY: Distressed that Baker's work has been "reviewed scurrillously because . . . many people . . . hate my work, and, I suppose, me"; offers various explanations for the critics' feelings. Discounts Nobel Prize rumors.

373. EH to Carlos Baker

Finca Vigia, Cuba, January 8, 1953
ALS, 2 pp.

SUMMARY: Busy with the film version of *The Old Man and the Sea* and trying to get "a good translation in Spanish." Disputes the "popular theory" that he was destroyed by a wound. Fun with the bears at the Ringling Brothers Circus; "I think I must feel or smell like a bear . . . we get along like brothers."

374. EH to Carlos Baker

Finca Vigia, Cuba, February 1, 1953
ALS, 2 pp.

SUMMARY: Commentary on the three critical studies of EH's life and work published in 1952 by Baker, Atkins, and Young, with particular emphasis on the latter's work. Enumerates Young's "lies and misstatements" with regard to the origins of short stories "Out of Season," "The Battler," "The Short Happy Life of Francis Macomber," "The Snows of Kilimanjaro," and "The Killers."

375. EH to Carlos Baker

Finca Vigia, Cuba, June 11, 1953
TLS, 3 pp.

SUMMARY: Swamped with letters since his Pulitzer Prize award, which has proven "wholly destructive and damaging to work." Has managed a piece for the Ringling Brothers *Program and Maga-*

zine for 1953. Angered by Yale professor, turned "amateur F.B.I. man," Charles Fenton's investigation of his "private life" in Oak Park. Reports plans for a trip to Europe and Africa and news of sons Patrick, Gregory, and "Bumby" (John). Further condemnation of Philip Young.

376. EH to Carlos Baker

Finca Vigia, Cuba, April 13, 195[5]
TLS, 2 pp.
SUMMARY: Since his Nobel Prize award, has been besieged by visitors, including four undergraduates from Princeton and a would-be writer from Rutgers. Expresses some anxiety about their possible portrayal of EH as "a bloody fool because he does not act or talk like Thomas Mann or Gide's Journals." Mentions new book on writers and writing by Malcolm Cowley, and planned trip aboard the *Pilar* to get away from people.

377. EH to Carlos Baker

"on board *Pilar*," May 2, 1955
ALS, 1 p.
SUMMARY: Pleased that Baker's book has sold out and that he is preparing a new edition. Taking off weight and working on a book about his recent African safari.

378. EH to Carlos Baker

Finca Vigia, Cuba, May 25, 1956
TLS, 1 p.
SUMMARY: Reports receipt of new edition of Baker's book upon return from Cabo Blanco, Peru, where he was shooting the film version of *The Old Man and the Sea*.

379. EH to Carlos Baker

Ketchum, Idaho, December 8, 1959
ALS, 3 pp.
SUMMARY: Discusses possible publication of Baker's book by Ernst Rowohlt, EH's German publisher. Mentions a "very touching and sad" autobiography by Harold Loeb, a writer-friend from the early years in Paris. Talk of the Cuban situation and his friendship with Spanish matador Antonio Ordóñez.

380. EH to Carlos Baker

Finca Vigia, Cuba, March 12, 1960

LS [in another hand], 2 pp.
SUMMARY: Further discussion of the advantages of publication by Rowohlt.

381. EH to Carlos Baker

Rochester, Minnesota, January 16, 1961
TLS, 1 p.
SUMMARY: Laid up with "some high book pressure trouble." Asks that Baker forward to the Modern Language Association his acceptance of invitation to serve on a program with Eliot, Camus, Perse, Sartre and Guillen. Comments on Charles Fenton's suicide.

382. EH to Carlos Baker

Rochester, Minnesota, January 20, 1961
TLS with holograph additions, 1 p.
SUMMARY: Preparing to leave St. Mary's Hospital for Ketchum. Looks forward to Baker's *Hemingway and His Critics: An International Anthology*. Background on "The Killers."

383. EH to Carlos Baker

Sun Valley, Idaho, January 26, 1961
Telegram, typed note on verso by Baker.
SUMMARY: Requests deletion from Baker anthology of an Ezra Pound quotation. In the typed note on verso of telegram, Baker confirms the deletion.

384. (Black Sun Press) Caresse Crosby to EH

Paris, France, [August 26, 1931]
ALS, 4 pp.
SUMMARY: Request from the publisher of the Black Sun Press for some original EH material for "a Black Sun Hemingway." Enclosed is writer Peter Neagoë's letter (No. 480), soliciting a contribution from EH for his anthology of expatriate American literature.

385. (Black Sun Press) EH to [Harry] Marks

Kansas City, Missouri, October 26, 1931
TLS, 1 p.
SUMMARY: Informs the American agent for the Black Sun Press that, although Mrs. Crosby may publish reprints of *In Our Time* and *The Torrents of Spring*, the idea of a Black Sun Hemingway is "definitely abandoned."

386. SB [Spruille Braden] to EH

Havana, Cuba, October 6, 1943
TL [carbon], 1 p.
SUMMARY: Returning *One World* by Wendell Willkie.

387. EH to Spruille [Braden]

[Finca Vigia, Cuba], November 18, 1943
TLS with holograph additions, 1 p.
SUMMARY: Intelligence report to the U.S. Ambassador to Cuba of possible renewed Falange activity on the island, citing as evidence the arrival from Spain of four members of the Carmelite Order.

388. EH to Spruille [Braden]

Finca Vigia, Cuba, December 2, 1943
TLS, 1 p.
SUMMARY: Report of the imminent arrival in Cuba of wealthy athlete and friend Winston Guest and the Marques de Comillas. Accompanying memorandum, "unsigned for obvious reasons," discusses a report by Gene Castro of U.S. plans for a "post war set-up," including a United States of South America, a United States of Central America, and a United States of North America. The U.S./Cuban narcotics trade is also mentioned.

389. EH to Louis and Mary [Bromfield]

[Schruns, Austria, ca. March 8, 1926]
ALS, 6 pp. CB194–196
SUMMARY: Describes a recent New York trip to end commitments with Horace Liveright of Boni & Liveright and sign with Maxwell Perkins of Scribner's for *The Torrents of Spring* and *The Sun Also Rises*. Mentions an offer from Harcourt Brace [Bromfield's publisher] which was rejected. References to Scott Fitzgerald, Glenway Wescott, Isabel Patterson, John Farrar, Ernest and Madeleine Boyd, Robert Benchley, Dorothy Parker, the Gerald Murphys, and Ford Madox Ford. Discusses the Owen Davis theatre adaptation of *The Great Gatsby*, *Manhattan Transfer* by John Dos Passos, and Anita Loos' *Gentlemen Prefer Blondes*, which EH notes is "sweeping the country like the flu of 1918."

390. EH to "Ned" [Edgar Calmer]

Key West, Florida, May 28, 1934
TLS, 3 pp.

SUMMARY: Advice to a young American journalist, working for the *Paris Herald*, on his fiction. Specific critiques of a novel and several short stories, with an offer to send some of Calmer's "better" material to Arnold Gingrich of *Esquire*.

391. EH to Edgar Calmer

Havana, Cuba, October 24, [P.M. 1934]
ALS, 2 pp.
SUMMARY: Short note mentioning an article for the December *Esquire*. Laments the rush of writers, including Dos Passos, to Hollywood; "they all do it because they have to eat—But . . . nobody has ever written anything worth a damn afterwards." Praise for John O'Hara's *Appointment in Samara*.

392. EH to Edgar Calmer

Havana, Cuba, May 19, [1935?]
ALS, 1 p.
SUMMARY: Encourages Calmer who is writing and holding down a job at the same time—". . . don't get discouraged. The old well always fills up if we don't dynamite it or anything."

393. EH to Edgar Calmer

Havana, Cuba, May 8, 1936
ALS, 3 pp.
SUMMARY: Discussion of a misunderstanding over money, with an offer to send more if needed. Sympathy on Calmer's failure to win a Guggenheim; "it looks as though you have to be a Communist to rate one now." Mentions story to appear in the June *Esquire*.

394. EH to Edgar Calmer

Key West, Florida, July 22, 1936
TLS with holograph additions, 1 p.
SUMMARY: Critique of one of Calmer's novels with caution: "Watch your use of slang. Slang goes sour so quickly." Expresses regret at not having been to college.

395. EH to Roger [Chase?]

Finca Vigia, Cuba, April 1, 1946
TLS, 1 p.
SUMMARY: Discussion of the fishing season with a fellow sportsman. Mentions his eldest son "Bumby" (John), a recently re-

turned German prisoner-of-war, and his marriage to Mary Welsh a month earlier.

396. EH to "Bill and Emily" [Nathan and Anne Davis]

Finca Vigia, Cuba, [ca. 1942]
TLS, 2 pp.
SUMMARY: Expresses regret that correspondents, a wealthy, expatriate couple living in Mexico City, are unable to visit the Finca. Research for *Men At War* is mentioned, along with some observations on the Mexican bullfight season, particularly matadors Silverio and Aruza. Discusses his wife Marty's difficulty with her novel *Liana*.

397. EH to Otto R. Demperwolf

Paris, France, June 24, [1927]
ALS, 1 p.
SUMMARY: "Delighted" response to a Brooklyn admirer who has asked EH to autograph a copy of *The Sun Also Rises*.

398. EH to [Lawrence] Drake

Paris, France, November 21, [1929]
ALS, 1 p.
SUMMARY: Thanks for Drake's letter and the copy of his book, published at the same time as *A Farewell to Arms*.

399. EH to "Yrene" [Irene Goldstein]

[Chicago, Illinois], March 16, [1921]
TLS, 1 p.
SUMMARY: Plans to get together in July with Goldstein, a friend from Petoskey. Mentions a recent trip to St. Louis ("canoed and fooled around the country club") and "a peach of an offer" from the *Toronto Star*. Time spent working hard and "having a regular orgy of bridge." Planned move to 100 E. Chicago Avenue. Signed: "Stein."

400. EH to Miriam Hapgood

[Lausanne, Switzerland], "Sunday" [ca. December 1922]
TLS, 1 p.
SUMMARY: Friendly reassurance to journalist Hutchen Hapgood's teenage daughter, who is in a Lausanne boarding school at the same time EH is covering the Lausanne Peace Conference for the

Toronto Star. Hopes she's "not too blue," reminding that he, her father and fellow journalists Guy Hickok and "Steff" (Lincoln Steffens) are only a few blocks away.

401. EH to Miriam Hapgood

[Lausanne, Switzerland], "The next Sunday" [ca. December 1922]

ALS, 2 pp.

SUMMARY: News of Hickok's and Steffens' departure and his wife Hadley's arrival, with invitation to come dine with them. Reports "working awfully hard at the conference." Letter (No. 400) and photographs enclosed.

402. EH to Miriam Hapgood

Schruns, Austria, January 12, 1925

ALS, 3 pp.

SUMMARY: Resumes correspondence with Miriam, now in Provincetown, Massachusetts, with her parents. Describes vacation in Schruns—"a nice little town full of devout, hard drinking people, good food and 36 noble varieties of beer." Mentions several long stories, "the best stuff I've done," written in the fall in Paris. Plans for a "book on the Bull Ring . . . with photographs" and illustrations by "somebody like Picasso."

403. EH to "HAYWIRE" [Leland Hayward]

Cabo Blanco, Peru, [ca. May 1956]

Telegram, signed.

SUMMARY: Reports successful filming of EH catching a 750-pound black marlin for the film version of *The Old Man and the Sea*.

404. EH to "Papa" [Clarence E. Hemingway]

Oak Park, Illinois, October 19, [19]08

ALS, 2 pp. CB xiii.

SUMMARY: Nine-year-old EH describes to his father, with misspellings, the activity in the school aquarium—a clam brought by EH from the Des Plaines River had shut on the tail of a Japanese fantail goldfish.

405. EH to Leicester Hemingway

Camaguey, Cuba, March 20, 1935

Telegram, 1 p.

SUMMARY: Advises brother on difficulties he will encounter on crossing from Florida to Cuba.

406. EH to "Baron" [Leicester Hemingway]

[Finca Vigia, Cuba], "Sunday," [1935]
ALS, 1 p.
SUMMARY: Instructions to his brother to get in touch upon his arrival in Cuba: "come out for a drink . . . have a letter for you from our mother."

407. EH to Mr. & Mrs. Leicester Hemingway

Bimini, Bahamas, June 13, 1936
Telegram, 1 p.
SUMMARY: "Love and best luck . . ."

408. EH to Leicester Hemingway

Malaga, Spain, September 14, 1959
AL (dictated), 4 pp., with ANS.
SUMMARY: Responds to his brother's plans to publish a book about the Hemingway family: "I thought that we [i.e. the family] were none of us to write about each other . . ." Ambivalent about the project. Requests seeing the manuscript before it is printed to determine "whether I can permit any letters by us to be published."

409. EH to "Mouse and Gig" [Patrick and Gregory Hemingway]

Cortina D'Ampezzo, Italy, December 14, 1948
TLS with holograph additions and ink drawing, 3 pp.
SUMMARY: Observations to EH's two younger sons on family and business matters and instructions concerning their forthcoming visit to Cuba. Describes vacation in northern Italy, with time spent shooting and in the company of old friends. Christmas greetings. Signed: "Papa."

410. EH to Betty Hogan

"enroute NY–New Orleans," December 19, [P.M. 1946]
ALS, 1 p.
SUMMARY: Response to New Jersey journalist's questionnaire on EH's early writing career.

411. EH to [Joseph M.] Hopkins

Key West, Florida, December 6, 1935
TLS with holograph additions, 1 p.
SUMMARY: Advice to Hopkins, a young American writer, on the craft of fiction. Offers to read anything Hopkins thinks is worth sending, but "until you have something other than *intention* to show don't expect a professional writer to spend time on your education."

412. EH to [Joseph M.] Hopkins

Key West, Florida, December 15, 1935
TLS with holograph additions, 2 pp.
SUMMARY: Recommends sending a story to Arnold Gingrich at *Esquire*, but with two factual corrections.

413. EH to [Joseph M.] Hopkins

Key West, Florida, December 24, 1935
TLS, 1 p.
SUMMARY: Critiques of two short stories.

414. EH to [Joseph M.] Hopkins

Key West, Florida, December 31, [1935]
TLS with holograph additions, 2 pp.
SUMMARY: Congratulations on selling a story to *Esquire*. Dismisses Hopkins' boast that he can write a better novel than *Madame Bovary*, as well as compliments on EH's work.

415. EH to [Joseph M.] Hopkins

Key West, Florida, February 6, 1936
TLS with holograph additions, 1 p.
SUMMARY: Discusses recently published "The Tradesman's Return," expressing some dissatisfaction with his choice of words. Complaint of too many visitors "destroying work and making you drink to put up with them rather than kill them."

416. EH to [Joseph M.] Hopkins

Key West, Florida, March 31, 1936
ALS, 2 pp.
SUMMARY: Words of encouragement for Hopkins, recounting his own early experience with publishers. Mentions the model for *The Sun Also Rises* heroine and the December 1922 theft in Paris of a valise containing all of his early manuscripts.

417. EH to Al [Horwits]

Finca Vigia, Cuba, August 13, 1948
TLS with holograph additions, 1 p.
SUMMARY: Gives impressions of Hollywood agent Horwits. Mentions his need for "a good lawyer," one who will "be as sound as he is fast and never outsmart himself or me." Talk of writing a story based on the Tony Zale–Rocky Graziano fight. Signed: "Mr. Papa."

418. EH to Al [Horwits]

Finca Vigia, Cuba, August 19, 1948
TLS, 2 pp.
SUMMARY: Asks opinion of Alfred Rice, who has become EH's attorney upon the death of Maurice Speiser. Talk of his trust and confidence in Horwits. Vivid description of the Sun Valley gambling escapades of Mark Hellinger, producer of the film version of "The Killers."

419. EH to Al [Horwits]

Finca Vigia, Cuba, October 3, 1949
TLS with holograph additions, 2 pp.
SUMMARY: Jokes about matching Miss Mary in a fight with Humphrey Bogart, "the Panda carrier." Discussion of novel-in-progress *Across the River and Into the Trees*, with request that Horwits handle negotiations for the movie rights. Sports talk.

420. EH to Al Horwits

Finca Vigia, Cuba, October 15, 1949
TLS ("Signed and forged by Miss Neta [Juanita Jensen, EH's secretary] without EH proofreading it"), 3 pp.
SUMMARY: Instructions to Horwits concerning their business relationship. Suggests that he delay a planned trip to Havana until completion of the novel; "I am fighting the last two rounds of a 20-round fight and am mean and very, very occupied." Details of the writing of *The Sun Also Rises*, "The Killers," and *For Whom the Bell Tolls*. Mentions A. E. Hotchner, "a very intelligent and honest boy," of Cosmopolitan, which will serialize *Across the River* (February 1950–June 1950). Boxing gossip and report of plans to sail to Europe aboard the *Île de France*.

421. EH to Al Horwits

Finca Vigia, Cuba, October 23, 1949

TLS with holograph additions, 1 p.

SUMMARY: Request that Horwits arrange passage on the *Île de France* and make sure there is no publicity. Mentions four-day fishing trip on the *Pilar*. Progress report on novel.

422. EH to Al Horwits

Havana, Cuba, November 5, 1949
Telegram.

SUMMARY: Instructions to finalize *Île de France* arrangements. Word count on novel with assessment that "stuff very good."

423. EH to Al Horwits

Venice, Italy, January 20, 1950
TLS with holograph additions, 2 pp.

SUMMARY: Reports *Across the River* manuscript now in the hands of Cosmopolitan's Hotchner, who has suggested deletion of an anti-Semitic paragraph. EH denies the charge, commenting "You know I am about as anti-semitic as [Yiddish novelist] Sholem Asch. . . ." Mentions attorney Alfred Rice and Hollywood producer David O. Selznik, regarding a movie deal for the novel. Talk of boxing and biking.

424. EH to Al Horwits

Venice, Italy, February 19, 1950
TLS with holograph additions, 1 p.

SUMMARY: Thanks for news clipping on Morrie Musselman, a high-school classmate with whom EH apparently collaborated on *Hokum*. Commentary on baseball and boxing. Reports Hotchner fired by Cosmopolitan because "they figured he was a better friend of mine than of the magazine's pocket book."

425. EH to Al Horwits

Finca Vigia, Cuba, December 4, 1950
TLS with holograph additions, 2 pp.

SUMMARY: Discussion of business matters, including a radio show version of "The Killers." Anecdote about Winston Guest. Comments on report by gossip columnist Louella Parsons that his marriage to Mary Welsh was breaking up over an Italian countess.

426. EH to Al Horwits

Finca Vigia, Cuba, November 20, 1951
TLS, 1 p.

SUMMARY: Mentions accepting "a very good deal" submitted by his attorney Alfred Rice [probably the movie contract for *Across the River*, which EH ultimately rejected]. Comic paragraph parodying a communist conspiracy involving Marx and Engels, boxers Tunney and Greb, the Harry K. Thaw-Stanford White society murder and Senator Joseph McCarthy.

427. EH to "Fever" [Howell G. Jenkins]

Petoskey, Michigan, [P.M. December 20, 1919]

TLS, 1 p. CB29–30. Typed on verso of "Wolves and Doughnuts," [ca. December 1919]. TMs [fragment], 1 p.

SUMMARY: Plans to get together in Chicago, "the city of sin, and sometimes gin," with Jenkins, a crony from Ambulance Service days in Italy. Mentions a job in Toronto, acting as companion to Ralph Connable, Jr., which "looks like the original Peruvian doughnuts." Signed: "Stein." Typed on verso of first page of an unpublished short story set in Chicago at the Café Cambrinus on Wabash Avenue. "Ernest M. Hemingway 602 State Street Petoskey, Michigan 3400 words" typed at head.

428. EH to "Carpative" [Howell G. Jenkins]

Paris, France, December 26, [1921]

ALS, 1 p. CB60.

SUMMARY: Christmas greetings. Describes room at the Hôtel Jacob and D'Angleterre "like a fine grog shop—Rheims, Asti Spumante and Cinzano Vermouth fill a shelf." Reports everything is "very cheap." Plans to buy a motorcycle with side car for "Bones" (Hadley). Signed: "Steen."

429. EH to "Carpative" [Howell G. Jenkins]

Paris, France, January 8, [1922]

ALS, 4 pp. CB61.

SUMMARY: Moving with "Hash" (Hadley) to apartment at 74 rue du Cardinal Lemoine, "in the best part of the Latin Quarter." Reports writing "a chunk of my novel and several articles." Although having "a priceless time," misses his male cronies; planned trip to Chamby-sur-Montreux in Switzerland "would be paradise with the men along." Signed: "Steen."

430. Herbert L. Matthews to EH

[New York, New York], August 24, 1960

TLS [carbon], 2 pp.

SUMMARY: Commentary on the Cuban Revolution, Fidel Castro, and the roles of Russia and the United States by a *New York Times* reporter who met EH in Madrid in 1937. Enclosed documents— a confidential report on Cuba for the *Times* and a paper written for the Stanford University *Hispanic American Record*—not included.

431. EH to Herbert Matthews

Ciudad Rodrigo, Spain, September 13, 1960
ALS, 2 pp.
SUMMARY: Apologies for the bother of "those fake reports" on EH's death. "When it really happens will be a miserable anti-climax." Characterizes the Cuban situation as "extremely complicated." Article by Herbert Matthews, "A New, Different Cuba," *New York Times*, September 19, 1974, is enclosed.

432. EH to Prudencio de Pereda

Key West, Florida, April 13, [P.M. 1934]
ACS.
SUMMARY: Encourages de Pereda, a young novelist, to continue writing. "If the stuff is good it always comes through but the editors can't tell the players without a score-card for a long, long time."

433. EH to Prudencio de Pereda

Key West, Florida, July 23, 1936
ALS, 1 p.
SUMMARY: Positive reaction to one of de Pereda's stories, with comment: ". . . we ought to have been in Spain all this week."

434. EH to Prudencio de Pereda

Key West, Florida, January 9, 1937
Telegram
SUMMARY: Notification of EH's plans to be in New York the following week.

435. EH to Prudencio de Pereda

New York, New York, June 24, 1938
Telegram.
SUMMARY: Arrangements for meeting at 15 East 48, Apartment 6B.

436. EH to Prudencio de Pereda

Sun Valley, Idaho, October 30, 1947
TLS with holograph additions, 1 p.
SUMMARY: Asks de Pereda to send galleys of *All the Girls We Loved*
for EH's review.

437. EH to Everett R. Perry

Key West, Florida, [ca. February 7, 1933]
ALS, 3 pp. CB380–381.
SUMMARY: Defense of the language in *Death in the Afternoon* to
Perry, Los Angeles City Librarian, arguing that it is used "to
convey to the reader a full and complete feeling of [the bullring],"
and not "to give gratuitous shock."

438. EH to Karl G. Pfeiffer

Piggott, Arkansas, January 1, [ca. 1934]
TC, 11 pp.
SUMMARY: Detailed advice to his brother-in-law (and hunting
companion) concerning wines he will encounter in Europe and
how they should be consumed. Comparisons of various national
beers, liqueurs, and other beverages. Advice on how to drink
burgundy and why to avoid "the various false absynthes." Pro-
tests that he is not "trying to make a drunkard out of my brother-
in-law" but is "merely summarizing [his] own experience" for
Pfeiffer's "doubtful benefit."

439. EH to Charles Poore

Finca Vigia, Cuba, August 8, 1949
TLS, 2 pp.
SUMMARY: Thanks to critic Poore and his associates at the *New
York Times Book Review* for printing EH's uncut "contribution"
(July 31, 1949, p. 1). Relates an unprintable "literary anecdote,"
detailing his 1944 Paris meeting with Jean-Paul Sartre, "a faintly
wormy character," and Simone de Beauvoir.

440. EH to Mr. Prentiss

Key West, Florida, February 22, 1936
TLS, 1 p.
SUMMARY: Accepts invitation to serve on the Cooper Memorial
Committee.

441. EH to "Capt. Willie" [William M. Rakow]

Aboard *Le Flandre*, June 29, [P.M. 1953]
ALS, 2 pp.
SUMMARY: Thanks to close friend—U.S. Naval Attaché in Havana for seeing EH and Mary off on the first leg of their African trip. Description of transatlantic crossing spent working out in the *Flandre*'s gymnasium and competing in trapshooting contests. Regards to Gregorio Fuentes, veteran mate, cook and caretaker of EH's fishing boat *Pilar*.

442. EH to William M. Rakow

Madrid, Spain, July 22, 1953
ALS, 1 p.
SUMMARY: News of Spain written from the same Madrid hotel, Hotel Florida, where EH stayed during the civil war. In Pamplona: ". . . a hell of a good party seven days and seven nights. . . . *The Sun Also Rises* gives you sort of a rough sketch." Offers some advice on fishing and speaks of a lighter (gift from Rakow) which he uses as "a lucky piece."

443. EH to William M. Rakow

Nairobi, Kenya, February 9, 1954
TLS with holograph additions, 1 p.
SUMMARY: Brief account of two airplane crashes in Uganda which prompted international reports of EH's death. Plans to join son Patrick, his wife and Miss Mary on the Kenya coast after completing "elephant survey."

444. EH to William M. Rakow

Venice, Italy, April 21, 1954
ALS, 3 pp.
SUMMARY: Fuller account of the crashes and resulting injuries. Mentions staying in Nairobi to dictate a *Look* piece (April 20, 1954, pp. 29–37; May 4, 1954, pp. 79–89). Then, on to the coast camp at Shimoni where fighting "a brush fire in a Force 7 wind" left him with serious burns. Receiving medical attention in Venice; plans for further treatment in Madrid.

445. EH to William M. Rakow

Madrid, Spain, May 19, 1954
ALS, 1 p.

SUMMARY: Anxious to get home to the Finca. Reports leak of April 21 letter to Associated Press, commenting "people probably think I'm a damn liar or publicity crazy."

446. EH to William M. Rakow

Aboard the *Francesco Morosini*, June 17, 1954
ALS, 1 p.
SUMMARY: Having a pleasant trip en route to Havana; "a little beat up," but "training good."

447. EH and Mary Hemingway to the William M. Rakows

[Finca Vigia, Cuba, ca. December 1954]
ACS
SUMMARY: Christmas greetings.

448. EH to William M. Rakow

Finca Vigia, Cuba, April 12, 1955
ALS, 1 p.
SUMMARY: Thoughts on the Nobel Prize: "The Swedish nonsense threw me out of stride by being overrun by jerks. . . ." Despite back pain, working well on new novel about his recent African safari.

449. EH to William M. Rakow

Finca Vigia, Cuba, December 6, 1955
TLS with holograph additions, 1 p.
SUMMARY: Talk of health and novel-in-progress. Thanks for gift of ashtray from Rakow's ship, the *Shenandoah*. Reports working hard on fishing sequences for the film version of *The Old Man and the Sea*.

450. EH and Mary Hemingway to the William M. Rakows

[Finca Vigia, Cuba, ca. Decenber 1955]
ACS
SUMMARY: Christmas greetings.

451. EH to Cranston D. Raymond

Aboard the *S.S. Volendam*, May 8, 1930
ALS, 2 pp.
SUMMARY: Gladly agrees to sign copies of his books for Raymond,

a young man, later with Scribner's, who provided bourbon and mystery stories for EH while he was hospitalized in Billings, Montana, following an automobile accident. "You were damn good to me . . . and I'll never forget it." Accompanying AC with inscription: "Postcard for the Kids." See also No. 497.

452. EH to B. G. Rudd

Finca Vigia, Cuba, April 13, 1956
ALS, 1 p.
SUMMARY: Grants permission to use "an extract from *Green Hills of Africa*" for a book Rudd is writing on western artist Charles M. Russell. Reminiscences of Red Lodge, Montana, with particular mention of "Chub" (Leland Stanford) Weaver, an old hunting companion, and the Wogoman brothers, "Mon" (Munroe) and Johnny.

453. EH to Herbert Ruhm

Finca Vigia, Cuba, October 10, 1950
TLS with holograph additions, 1 p.
SUMMARY: Discusses with Ruhm, a young writer, the negative reviews of *Across the River and Into the Trees*, speculating that his "pride, rudeness, and various other sins" may be to blame. Enumerates that which inspires his respect, including "honest whores, all good servants, good ball players, cats, good dogs." Likes German authors Thomas Mann, Frederick the Great, Maurice de Saxe, Goethe, and Hans Sachs.

454. EH to Herbert Ruhm

Finca Vigia, Cuba, January 6, 195[1]
TLS, 2 pp.
SUMMARY: Reports completion of book one of his "triple decker" novel about the sea, later part of *Islands in the Stream*. Commentary on the Spanish-American War and extensive recommendations on military literature. Mentions his article on the Ezzard Charles–Joe Louis heavyweight championship fight in *National Police Gazette* (January 1951, p. 16). Anecdote about Ford Madox Ford, soldier-friend Chink Dorman-Smith, and himself.

455. EH to Herbert Ruhm

Finca Vigia, Cuba, June 21, 1952
TLS, 1 p.
SUMMARY: New book, *The Old Man and the Sea*, coming out

September 8th. Reports photographer Alfred Eisenstaedt down to take color portraits for the cover of *Life*, featuring a pre-publication printing of the novel (September 1, 1952, pp. 35–54). Comments on boxing and Fitzgerald's writing.

456. EH to Herbert Ruhm

Finca Vigia, Cuba, September 11, 1952
TLS with holograph additions, 1 p.
SUMMARY: Mentions legal problems with Ballantine Ale Company regarding an unauthorized advertisement. Boxing gossip. Signed: "Hemingstein."

457. EH to Herbert Ruhm

Finca Vigia, Cuba, April 20, 1953
ALS, 1 p.
SUMMARY: Apologies for not answering Ruhm's last letter. Reports African trip delayed.

458. EH to Mrs. [E. S.] Russell

Cooke, Montana, October 27, 1936
TLS, 1 p.
SUMMARY: Discusses the health, talents, and character of Tom Shevlin, a close friend and fellow sportsman though fifteen years EH's junior, with correspondent who is likely Shevlin's mother-in-law.

459. EH to Harry Saltpeter

Key West, Florida, April 16, 1936
TLS with holograph additions, 2 pp.
SUMMARY: Responds to an inquiry regarding painter-friend Waldo Peirce, relating several printable anecdotes.

460. EH to Marion [Smith]

Venice, Italy, [ca. 1948–1950]
TL, 1 p.
SUMMARY: Response to the wife of close friend Bill Smith, asking her to forward a manuscript, possibly one of those stolen in Paris in December 1922. Reassurances about the "loyalty check," noting "they cannot be suspicious of Bill about Dos [Passos] since Dos is a pillar of Conservatism and I don't mean salt."

461. EH to "Salesman Smith" [William Smith]

Petoskey, Michigan, December 4, [1919]

TL, 1 p. Smith has used verso for his reply, n.p., n.d.

SUMMARY: Reports to Smith, a close friend from boyhood, on the publication potential of his early writing attempts, including short stories "Wolves and Doughnuts" and "The Woppian Way," later "The Passing of Pickles McCarty." Description of a young waitress who, according to EH, "has fallen for the writer." Signed: "Wemage" in type.

462. EH to "Bill" [William Smith]

Schruns, Austria, January 28, [1925]

ALS, 2 pp.

SUMMARY: Responds to Smith's query concerning Paris employment possibilities with news of a job opening as secretary to Dr. W. Dawson Johnstone, Librarian, American Library of Paris— "1500 francs a month" for "all stuff you could do while shaving." Points out that "fewer people die in libraries than are killed everyday in the steel industry." Signed: "Hollow Bone."

463. EH to [William] Smith

[Schruns, Austria], February 14, [1925]

ALS, 4 pp.

SUMMARY: Expresses disappointment that the American Library job fell through, but will continue looking. Describes winter holiday spent skiing, drinking and playing poker at "the hut" (the Madlenerhaus in the Silvretta Range). Lengthy diatribe against homosexuals on the literary scene; "they're organized like the Masons." Defends his passion for bullfighting, arguing that it's not "a moral spectacle," just "a hell of a wonderful show." Signed: "Immer."

464. EH to [William] Smith

[Paris, France], December 3, 1925

TL, 2 pp. Typed on verso of European shipping trade report.

SUMMARY: Reports completion of *The Torrents of Spring*, a "funny book" which "Scott [Fitzgerald], Louis Bromfield, Dos [Passos] etc. declare . . . is K.O." Observations on the fierce competition in the "Mag world" to get "exclusivity on authors," especially Fitzgerald. Describes "some A1 drinking" escapades with Pauline Pfeiffer, fashion editor of the Paris edition of *Vogue*. Mentions the

Gerald Murphys, a wealthy American couple with whom he and Hadley have been invited to visit at Cap d'Antibes on the Riviera. Photographs of Pamplona bullfight enclosed. Signed: "yrs Miller" in type.

465. EH to Arthur S. Teague

Finca Vigia, Cuba, August 10, 1951
TLS, 1 p.
SUMMARY: Agrees to write "a piece on 'the cog-wheel railway' " for Teague, a close friend from the 22nd Infantry Regiment during World War II. Busy revising the first book of his sea novel, later part of *Islands in the Stream*.

466. EH to Thomas Tibbitts

Finca Vigia, Cuba, January 20, 1953
ALS, 1 p.
SUMMARY: Reply to a Battle Creek, Michigan, Hemingway collector, expressing his hope that the books will be "worth collecting." Confirms his true birthdate as July 21, 1899, admitting he lied about his age "to get jobs and in the 1st war." Recommends Lee Samuels' bibliography.

467. EH to "Jack" [John N. Wheeler?]

Cortina d'Ampezzo, Italy, March 7, 1949
TLS with holograph additions, 1 p.
SUMMARY: Rejects an idea [possibly submitted through John Wheeler, the general manager of the North American Newspaper Alliance] for an honorary republication of his early writings, commenting "the hell with pitching for honor if there is money involved and it isn't a benefit." Boxing gossip.

468. [Unnamed secretary of G. A. Pfeiffer] to EH

[n.p.], October 24, 1932.
TL [carbon], 1 p.
SUMMARY: Acknowledges delivery of a copy of *Death in the Afternoon* autographed by EH for "Uncle Gus." Enclosed with No. 37.

469. EH and Mary Hemingway to [Unknown]

[n.p., n.d.]
ACS, with black and white photograph of the *Pilar*.
SUMMARY: Christmas greetings.

470. EH and Mary Hemingway to [Unknown]

[n.p., n.d.]

ACS, with sketch of the Plaza de la Cathedral, Havana.

SUMMARY: Christmas greetings.

471. EH to "Queridos hermanos y companeros"

San Francisco de Paula, Cuba, [1940]

TL, 1 p.

SUMMARY: Describes sports in Cuba. Explains jai alai betting, tells who the good players are. Mentions Marty [his wife, Martha Gellhorn]. Refers to his novel in progress [*For Whom the Bell Tolls*]: "It will be a year tomorrow that I have written on this book."

472. EH to "Citizens"

[Cuba, 1940]

ALS, 1 p.

SUMMARY: Having looked in vain for them on the boat, invites friends for tennis and drinks.

PART III:B

MANUSCRIPTS AND DOCUMENTS

---

473. Untitled poem, [ca. 1918-1920]

AMs in pencil with revisions, 2 pp.

SUMMARY: Twenty-three line, four-stanza poem beginning "There was Ike and Tony and Jaque and me . . .;" a ballad about soldiers on leave in the Italian town of Schio during the close of World War I. First three stanzas published in *88 Poems*, edited by Nicholas Gerogiannis, p. 18. New York: Harcourt Brace Jovanovich; Bruccoli Clark, 1979.

474. "The Age Demanded," [ca. 1928]

AMsS in ink, 1 p.

SUMMARY: Eight-line, four-stanza poem, with added message above dated from Paris, March 15, about *Der Querschnitt* editor Alfred Flechtheim: "God bless Flechtheim! to whom I owe 100 dollars (cash) and much more in many other ways. But will pay the money within the year and wish you all happiness always. Ernest Hemingway." Added line beneath the poem "(But not by Flechtheim!)." A portrait of Hemingway is in the upper left hand corner of the folio sheet and a Pacific [steamship] Line sticker pasted below. "An Age Demanded" was originally published in *Der Querschnitt* 5 (1925): 111; this text was prepared for *Der Querschnitt* 8 (1928), a Festschrift issue honoring Flechtheim.

475. "The Sea Change," [ca. 1930]

TMsS [initialled] with revisions in pencil, 5 pp.

SUMMARY: Adaptation for a stage reading of short story of the same title. Characters: Narrator, Man, Woman, James. Unpublished in this form.

476. "An Old Newspaperman Writes or The Boys Should Know Their Stuff," [ca. 1934]

TMs with revisions in pencil, 9 pp.

SUMMARY: Article on contemporary journalism. Published under the title "Old Newsman Writes: A Letter from Cuba," in *Esquire*, December 1934, pp. 25–26.

477. "Remembering Shooting-Flying: A Key West Letter," [ca. 1934-1935]

TMsS with revisions in pencil, 7 pp.

SUMMARY: Article on hunting in Illinois, the Vorarlberg, Clark's Fork, Wyoming, and elsewhere. Titled in pencil with notation "By Ernest Hemingway. 1st serial rights only." Published in *Esquire*, February 1935, p. 21.

478. ["Sailfish Off Mombasa: A Key West Letter," ca. 1934-1935]

TMs with revisions in pencil and ink, 8 pp.

SUMMARY: Article on fishing in East Africa. Typed notation: "Copyright by Ernest Hemingway. First U.S. Serial Rights Only." Published in *Esquire*, March 1935, p. 25.

479. "Life and Letters, a Manuscript Found in a Bottle," January 15, 1935

TMs with revisions in pencil, 6 pp.

SUMMARY: A satire on contemporary writers, including Gilbert Seldes, Alexander Woollcott, James Joyce, and William Saroyan. Seldes: "Let me read Seldes if I want to. It's no worse than a bad cold." Anecdote about Woollcott and General John J. Pershing. Joyce: "I'll tell you about my pal James Joyce, we've been drunk with him more than eleven times." Attack on Saroyan, "who tells the boys in his stories he can write like, or better than, other people. . . ." Published in *Esquire*, January, 1935, p. 159.

480. "A New York Letter," [ca. 1935]

TMs with revisions in pencil, 6 pp.

SUMMARY: Article on the Joe Louis–Max Baer prizefight, September 24, 1935, in New York. Titled in pencil with typed notation "Ernest Hemingway. First U.S. serial rights only." Published under the title "Million Dollar Fight: A New York Letter," in *Esquire*, December 1935, p. 35.

481. "The Tradesman's Return," [ca. 1935-1936]

TMsS with revisions in pencil, 15 pp.

SUMMARY: Short story which later became Part II of *To Have and*

Have Not. Notation in pencil: "By Ernest Hemingway. 1st U.S. serial rights, only. 4270 words." Published in *Esquire*, February 1936, p. 27.

482. ["The Time Now, The Place Spain," ca. 1938]

TMs with revisions in pencil, 6 pp.

SUMMARY: Article on the Spanish Civil War. Notation in pencil: "Send to Arnold Gingrich, air-mail—registered—special delivery, 1515 North State Parkway, Chicago, Illinois." Published in *Ken*, April 7, 1938, pp. 36–37. Accompanying notes in another hand: 1 page summary of the article and 1 page statement on EH's position with *Ken* (this appeared as a boxed notice on p. 37 of the first issue).

483. "The Next Outbreak of Peace," ca. 1938-1939

TMsS with revisions in pencil, 5 pp.

SUMMARY: Article on Neville Chamberlain's policy of appeasement. Notation in pencil: "Ernest Hemingway, 1st U.S. Serial Rights only." Published in *Ken*, January 12, 1939, pp. 12–13. See also No. 423.

484. Last Will and Testament of Ernest M. Hemingway

Chicago, Illinois, December 3, 1921

TDS, 2 pp.

SUMMARY: Will bequeaths Hemingway's entire estate to his first wife, Elizabeth Hadley Richardson Hemingway. If she does not survive him, the estate goes to the lawful issue of their marriage. If no children survive him, the estate is to be divided among EH's three sisters, or their issue. Signed by EH on each page and at the conclusion by three witnesses. Accompanying news clip dated August 1961, concerning the 1955 will put into effect upon EH's death.

485. Check made out to EH for £150 from Anthony B. Jenkinson

November 6, 1941.

Endorsed.

486. EH to [Unknown]

[n.p., n.d.]

AC, photograph of Golmerjoch, Switzerland.

SUMMARY: Mentions skiing.

PART III:C

CORRESPONDENCE RELATING TO

HEMINGWAY

---

487. Carlos Baker to Arthur S. Teague

Princeton, New Jersey, December 28, 1961
TLS, 1 p.
SUMMARY: Request to Teague, EH's comrade in the 22nd Infantry Regiment, for reminiscences of the war years as part of research for *Ernest Hemingway: A Life Story*.

488. Carlos Baker to Paul Romaine

[n.p.], December 30, 1963
TLS, 1 p.
SUMMARY: Forwarding copy of *The Legacy of Abner Green: A Memorial Journal* to the Milwaukee bookseller who published William Faulkner's *Salmagundi* with EH's poem "Ultimately" on the back cover.

489. (Black Sun Press) Caresse [Crosby] to Archibald MacLeish

Paris, France, April 3, 1931
Telegram. Holograph note on verso from MacLeish to EH, n.p., n.d.
SUMMARY: Offer to EH, through his agent MacLeish, from the publisher of the Black Sun Press of $1000 advance for an unpublished work; "but must know conditions" with regard to exclusive rights, limited edition, signed copies and the like. In a holograph note on the verso of the telegram, MacLeish informs EH of his reply to Crosby that "1500 would be the minimum."

490. (Black Sun Press) Peter Neagoë to [Caresse] Crosby

Paris, France, August 12, 1931
ALS, 3 pp.

SUMMARY: Discussion of planned anthology to include a selection from *Shadows of the Sun* by Mrs. Crosby's late husband, Harry; and a request for her help in securing a contribution from EH as well, recognizing the anthology's "incompleteness without a selection from him."

491. EOB [Ellis O. Briggs] to J. West

[Havana, Cuba], January 7, 1944

TLS [carbon, initialled] with holograph additions, 1 p.

SUMMARY: U.S. Embassy memorandum summarizing EH's letter (No. 387) to Spruille Braden, November 18, 1943, reporting renewed Falange activity in Cuba.

492. Adrian H. Goldstone to Lee Samuels

[n.p.], November 22, 1957

TL [carbon], 1 p.

SUMMARY: At the insistence of mutual friend Marston Drake, Goldstone calls bibliographer Samuels' attention to "a reproduction of a letter by EH that appeared in the 1948 catalog of La Casa Belga in [Havana]" and "what is probably an unauthorized publication of the collected poems of Ernest Hemingway." Offers to send copy of Reginald Rowe catalogue. Enclosed with No. 278.

493. Grace Hall Hemingway to "Husband" [Clarence E. Hemingway]

Oak Park, Illinois, October 19, [19]08.

ALS, 3 pp.

SUMMARY: Family news to EH's father who, after a four-month post-graduate course in obstetrics at the New York Lying-In Hospital, is returning home via New Orleans. EH's letter (No. 404) enclosed.

494. Grace Hall Hemingway to Duttons, Inc.

River Forest, Illinois, January 18, 1939

ALS, 2 pp.

SUMMARY: Offers for sale two copies of the 1917 Oak Park High School *Senior Tabula* containing the "Class Prophecy" by EH.

495. Mary Hemingway to Carlos Baker

Finca Vigia, Cuba, [ca. September 2, 1952]

TLS, 1 p.

SUMMARY: Praise for Baker's *Hemingway: The Writer As Artist*.

496. Garfield D. Merner to "Uncle Gus" [G. A. Pfeiffer]

[n.p.], July 27, 1938
TL [carbon], 1 p.
SUMMARY: Acknowledges receipt of No. 66 of the limited first
edition of *The Spanish Earth*. Enclosed with No. 48.

497. Cranston D. Raymond to [Unknown]

Seattle, Washington, July 4, 1961
TLS, 1 p.
SUMMARY: Description of Raymond's 1930 introduction to EH
in a Billings, Montana hospital. See also No. 446.

PART IV

Miscellaneous

PART IV

MISCELLANEOUS

---

498. Bust of Ernest M. Hemingway by Robert Berks (1959)

Cast metal, 22 inches high, mounted on a marble base.

499. Black and white photograph of Ernest M. Hemingway

13½ x 10½ inches. INSCRIBED: "To Willie Rakow best always from his friend Ernest Hemingway Havana 9/8/54."

COLOPHON

THIS catalogue was printed by the Arion Press in San Francisco, under the direction of Andrew Hoyem, from Monotype composition in Baskerville by MacKenzie-Harris Corp., on French mould-made Rives paper, with photolithography by Phelps-Schaefer Litho-Graphics Company, and binding by the Schuberth Bookbindery. The edition is limited to 150 copies in full cloth, 50 copies in quarter leather. Completed Spring 1985.